THE Brainteasers TRIVIA QUIZBOOK

Gyles Brandreth

with illustrations by
Nick Berringer and Mike Miller

TREASURE PRESS

First published in Great Britain as three separate volumes

Family Quiz Book 1
First published by Hamlyn Paperbacks
Copyright © 1979 Victorama Limited

1000 Questions - the Greatest Quiz Book Ever Known
First published by Transworld Publishers Ltd
Text copyright © Gyles Brandreth 1980
Illustration copyright © Transworld Publishers 1980

1000 Brainteasers - Mind Bogglers to Boggle Your Mind
First published by Transworld Publishers Ltd
Text copyright © 1984 Victorama Ltd
Illustration copyright © 1984 Transworld Publishers Ltd

This omnibus edition published in Great Britain in 1991 by
Treasure Press
Michelin House
81 Fulham Road
London SW3 6RB

ISBN : 1 85051 631 6

Printed in Czechoslovakia

50735/02

CONTENTS

PART ONE

500 QUESTION QUIZ

I

All Stars

1 Peter O'Toole played the same English king in both *Becket* and *The Lion in Winter*.
Was it:

        Stephen
        Alfred the Great
        Edward I
        Henry II

2 Who was swallowed by the killer shark in *Jaws*?
Was it:

        Richard Dreyfuss
        Warren Beatty
        Robert Shaw
        Farah Fawcett-Majors

3 Which actress played the part of Dick Van Dyke's wife in *The Dick Van Dyke Show* on television in the 1960s?
Was it:

        Mary Tyler Moore
        Lucille Ball
        Elizabeth Taylor
        Goldie Hawn

4 When Humphrey Bogart asked Dooley Wilson to play 'As Time Goes By' in *Casablanca* what were the memorable words he said?

Were they:

> 'Play it again, man'
> 'Play that again, Sam'
> 'Play it, Sam'
> 'Play it again, Sam'

5 How many children did Maria (Julie Andrews) have to look after in *The Sound of Music*?
Were there:

> Four children
> Seven children
> Twelve children
> Ten children

6 For which of his films did Marlon Brando win an Oscar in 1954?
Was it:

> *On The Waterfront*
> *A Streetcar Named Desire*
> *Julius Caesar*
> *The Wild One*

7 Who starred in the comedy *Gentlemen Prefer Blondes*?
Was it:

> Alice White
> Ruth Taylor
> Marilyn Monroe
> Jane Russell

8 Who played secret agent James Bond in the 1966 film of *Casino Royale*?
Was it:

> Roger Moore
> George Lazenby
> David Niven
> Sean Connery

9 Which actress played the female lead in the film of D. H. Lawrence's story *The Virgin and The Gypsy*?

Was it:

> Julie Christie
> Joanna Shimkus
> Glenda Jackson
> Susannah York

10 Marilyn Monroe was married to a famous American playwright during the 1950s.
Was it:

> Tennessee Williams
> Eugene O'Neill
> Edward Albee
> Arthur Miller

2

The Ancient World

1 Who became the first emperor of Rome in 27 B.C.?
Was it:

        Romulus
        Tarquin
        Octavius Caesar
        Tiberius Caesar

2 What nationality was the great general Hannibal?
Was he:

        Greek
        Carthaginian
        Spanish
        Persian

3 Who jumped out of his bath and ran naked through the streets of Syracuse shouting 'Eureka!'?
Was it:

        Archimedes
        Tutankhamun
        Nero
        Homer

4 What was the name of the public meeting place in Rome, used for trade and political gatherings?
Was it:

        The Colosseum
        The Parthenon

The Forum
The Salarium

5 Which legendary hero left the ruins of Troy and sailed to
Italy to found the city of Rome?
Was it:

      Remus
      Ulysses
      Apollo
      Aeneas

6 Alexander the Great was king of which part of Greece?
Was it:

      The Peloponnesus
      Macedonia
      Athens
      Crete

7 For what is Virgil best remembered?
Is it for:

      Poetry
      Orgies
      Engineering
      His love for Cleopatra

8 Who crossed the river Rubicon with his army in 49 B.C.
and started a civil war in Italy?
Was it:

      Brutus
      Cassius
      Julius Caesar
      Pompey

9 Which Greek philosopher was condemned to death in
Athens in 399 B.C. because his teachings were contrary to
established beliefs?
Was it:

      Plato
      Galen

Epicurus
Socrates

10 What was a 'trireme'?
Was it:

        A sword
        A drinking song
        A ship
        A leader of the peasants in Rome

3

Men at the Top

1 Who was the youngest British Prime Minister, who took office when he was only twenty-four?
Was it:

> Benjamin Disraeli
> David Lloyd George
> William Pitt (the younger)
> Stanley Baldwin

2 Who was Trygve Lie?
Was he:

> The leader of the Norwegian Resistance in the Second World War
> The first Secretary-General of the United Nations
> The hero king of Norway who defeated the Danes
> The leader of the first expedition to the North Pole

3 Who was the first Chancellor of West Germany?
Was it:

> Adolf Hitler
> Willy Brandt
> Kurt Weill
> Konrad Adenauer

4 Who controlled the government of China before Mao Tse-Tung?

Was it:

Chou-en Lai
Chiang Kai-chek
The Gang of Four
The last Manchu empress

5 Who is the Chairman of the International Olympic Committee?
Is it:

Sir Roger Bannister
Avery Brundage
Kurt Waldheim
Lord Killanin

6 Who was leader of the British Labour Party before Sir Harold Wilson took over in 1963?
Was it:

Clement Attlee
Hugh Gaitskell
Jo Grimond
George Brown

7 Who was the only English Pope?
Was it:

Adrian IV
Boniface VIII
Leo VI
Urban II

8 Alexander Dubcek was leader of which East European country in the 1960s?
Was it:

East Germany
Romania
Hungary
Czechoslovakia

9 Marshall Jean-Bédel Bokassa is Head-of-State in which African country?

Is it:

  Niger
  Botswana
  Central African Empire
  Chad

10 What is the name of the Chief Cashier of the Bank of England, whose signature appears on every English bank note printed after February 1970?
Is it:

  J. S. Fforde
  D. W. Healey
  J. Q. Hollom
  J. B. Page

4

Brave New World

1 In which American city was John F. Kennedy assassinated in 1963?
Was it:

        Houston
        Phoenix
        Dallas
        Las Vegas

2 Alaska has not always belonged to the U.S.A. From whom did the American government buy the territory in 1867?
Was it:

        Russia
        Canada
        Great Britain
        Norway

3 Who was the commander of the British army which surrendered to George Washington at Yorktown in 1781, during the American War of Independence (American Revolution)?
Was it:

        Sir Arthur Wellesley
        Sir John Moore
        General Wolfe
        Lord Cornwallis

4 What was New York called before it was given its present name?

Was it:

>   New London
>   New Paris
>   New Copenhagen
>   New Amsterdam

5 What was the 'Alamo'?
Was it:

>   An American Indian tribe
>   A nickname for General Eisenhower
>   A Texan garrison massacred by Mexicans
>   The ship carrying the tea in the Boston 'Tea Party'

6 Who commanded the Confederate armies during the American Civil War?
Was it:

>   William Sherman
>   Robert E. Lee
>   Richard Gatling
>   George Washington

7 Where is Pearl Harbor?
Is it:

>   In the Caroline Islands
>   On the coast of Papua New Guinea
>   In the Hawaiian Islands
>   In American Samoa

8 Which early explorer discovered the American mainland first, and gave his christian name to the continent?
Was it:

>   Amerigo Magellan
>   Amerigo Vespucci
>   Amerigo Cabot
>   Amerigo Columbus

9 Neil Armstrong was the first American to set foot on the moon, but who was the first American to walk in space?

Was it:

>Edward H. White
>John Glenn
>Michael Collins
>Thomas P. Stafford

10 Why do we remember the name Francis Gary Powers?
Was he:

>The first American astronaut to orbit the earth
>Abraham Lincoln's assassin
>The pilot of a spy plane shot down in 1960
>The pilot who dropped the H-bomb on Hiroshima

5

Colour Conscious

1 What is the colour for danger in scientific laboratories?
Is it:

> Red
> Dark brown
> Bright yellow
> White

2 Where was the notorious 'Black Hole', which caused outrage among the British public in 1756?
Was it:

> In Newgate Prison
> In Calcutta
> In Cawnpore
> In Boston

3 Which famous German actress starred in the *The Blue Angel* and sang 'Falling in Love Again'?
Was it:

> Candice Bergen
> Elisabeth Bergner
> Marlene Dietrich
> Elisabeth Schwarzkopf

4 What are the 'Red Arrows'?
Are they:

> A punk rock group
> The instruments used by a tattooist
> An urban guerrilla group
> An R.A.F. display team

5 What is a 'blue-stocking'?
Is it:

> A literary and studious woman
> An article of policewomen's lingerie
> An Oxford University rowing sock
> A sailor's shroud

6 What is the name of the race-horse which won the English
Grand National in 1973 and 1974, and again in 1977?
Is it:

> Blue Boy
> Green Giant
> Red Rum
> Pink Panther

7 What were the 'Black and Tans'?
Were they:

> A multi-racial religious sect
> A British military force
> A Red Indian tribe
> Indian missionaries

8 What is a 'purple passage'?
Is it:

> A rough sea crossing
> A narrow street in Rome
> An excessively sentimental piece of writing
> An apoplectic fit

9 Where would you find a 'green room'?
Is it:

> At a race-course

In a casino
In a theatre
At a botanical garden

10 The blue-shirts were supporters of which Fascist leader
of the 1930s?
Was it:

Francisco Franco
Adolf Hitler
Benito Mussolini
Sir Oswald Mosley

6

All at Sea

1 Where would you expect to find the Skagerrak?
Is it:

> In the Arctic
> In the South China Sea
> Between the North Sea and the Baltic
> At the entrance to Hudson Bay

2 Where was the Battle of the River Plate fought?
Was it:

> In the Atlantic off the coast of South America
> In the Coral Sea off the coast of Australia
> In the Mediterranean off the coast of Crete
> In the Atlantic off the coast of Senegal

3 Which land mass is nearest to the island of St Helena
where Napoleon Bonaparte spent his final years?
Is it:

> Antarctica
> Africa
> The Italian peninsular
> South America

4 What was the name of the British Atlantic passenger liner
which sank in the North Atlantic in 1912 on her maiden
voyage?

Was she:

> The *Titanic*
> The *Marie Celeste*
> The *Lusitania*
> The *Mauretania*

5 Which intrepid navigator and his crew first sailed round the Cape of Good Hope in 1487, when it was called the Cape of Storms?
Was it:

> Hernan Cortés
> Sir Francis Drake
> Bartholomew Diaz
> Sebastian del Cano

6 If you sailed from the Black Sea into the Aegean which stretch of water would you pass through?
Is it:

> The Sea of Marmara
> The Gulf of Corinth
> The Dardanelles
> The Bosporus

7 What is the name of the famous French oceanographer and marine biologist?
Is it:

> Jacques Clouseau
> Charles Boyer
> Jean-Yves Terlain
> Jacques-Yves Cousteau

8 For what is the Sargasso Sea best known?
Is it:

> Strong currents
> The unexplained disappearance of ships and planes
> Seaweed
> The launching of the first submarine Polaris missile

9 What was the 'mosquito armada'?
Was it:

> The Lilliputian fleet encountered by Gulliver
> The ships which evacuated troops from Dunkirk
> The English ships which fought the Spanish Armada
> The German U-boat fleet in the Second World War

10 What is the Plimsoll line?
Is it:

> A nickname for the Equator
> The instrument used for sounding depths at sea
> A mark on the hulls of merchant ships
> The mark on a sailor's rum glass in the Royal Navy

7
Myths and Legends

1 Who was the Nordic god of thunder who gave his name to a day of the week in English?
Was it:

Tiw
Thor
Saturn
Woden

2 Which legendary Greek king commanded the Greek armies at the siege of Troy?
Was it:

Menelaus
Achilles
Agamemnon
Hector

3 What was Valhalla in Scandinavian mythology?
Was it:

The name for the sun god
America
The resting place of warriors killed in battle
The name of the constellation of Orion

4 Which of King Arthur's knights received the Holy Grail?
Was it:

>Sir Lancelot
>Sir Galahad
>Sir Kay
>Sir Bevedere

5 According to ancient legends an African king is still supporting the sky. What is his name?
Is it:

>Atlas
>Ajax
>Amin
>Ammon

6 Venus was the Roman goddess of love, but what did the Greeks call her?
Was it:

>Athene
>Prosperine
>Aphrodite
>Calypso

7 What did Pandora release when she opened her box?
Was it:

>Sunshine
>Troubles and misery
>A handsome youth
>A flock of doves

8 Who flew too near to the sun and melted the wax binding his wings, which caused him to plunge into the sea and drown?
Was it:

>Mercury
>Icarus
>Ixion
>Phaeton

9 Which twentieth-century play takes its title from a legendary king of Cyprus who fell in love with a statue?
Is it:

Pygmalion
Dear Brutus
Jumpers
Puntila

10 Who was the mythical musician who went into Hades to rescue his wife by charming the infernal spirits with his playing?
Was he:

Pan
Nero
Euripides
Orpheus

8

Who Said?

1 Which statesman said: 'You can fool all the people some of the time, and some of the people all of the time, but you cannot fool all the people all of the time'?

Was it:

        Charles de Gaulle
        Sir Harold Wilson
        Abraham Lincoln
        Richard Nixon

2 Which of Shakespeare's characters says: 'All the world's a stage, and all the men and women merely players'?

Is it:

        Jaques, in *As You Like It*
        Macbeth, in *Macbeth*
        Hamlet, in *Hamlet*
        Portia, in *The Merchant of Venice*

3 With what words did the journalist and explorer Sir Henry Morton Stanley greet the lost explorer David Livingstone, in Africa?

Did he say:

        'Hello Dr Livingstone.'
        'It's Dr Livingstone isn't it?'
        'Dr Livingstone, I presume.'
        'Dr Livingstone, I imagine.'

4 On what occasion is the Duke of Wellington credited with saying: 'Up, guards, and at them!'?
Was it:

> At the Peterloo riots at Manchester in 1819
> At the ball on the eve of Waterloo
> During the advance of the French infantry at Waterloo
> At the battle of Talavera

5 Which film actress said: 'Come up and see me sometime.'?
Was it:

> Brigitte Bardot
> Mae West
> Hattie Jacques
> Marilyn Monroe

6 To whom did Benjamin Disraeli reputedly say: 'We writers, ma'am'?
Was it:

> Jane Austen
> His wife
> Queen Victoria
> George Eliot

7 Who was Christopher Marlowe describing when he put these words into Faustus's mouth: 'Was this the face that launched a thousand ships, /And burnt the topless towers of Ilium'?
Was it:

> Helen of Troy
> Dido, Queen of Carthage
> Mary, Queen of Scots,
> Anne Boleyn

8 In which television series were these words often repeated: 'Sock it to me, sock it to me, sock it to me'?
Was it:

> *Monty Python's Flying Circus*
> *The Lucy Show*
> *Rowan and Martin's Laugh-In*
> *Perry Mason*

9 To what incident in the Second World War was Winston Churchill referring when he said: 'This is not the end. It is not even the beginning of the end. But it is, perhaps, the end of the beginning.'?
Was it:

> The evacuation from Dunkirk
> The Battle of Egypt
> The Battle of Britain
> The invasion of Normandy

10 Who said: 'The end justifies the means'?
Was it:

> Joan of Arc
> Anthony Wedgwood Benn
> Niccolò Machiavelli
> Napoleon Bonaparte

9

Highspots

1 Mount Everest is the highest mountain in the world, but what is the second highest?
    Is it:
        Annapurna
        Mont Blanc
        K.2.
        Chogori

2 In which American state is Mount McKinley, the highest mountain in North America?
Is it:
        Alaska
        Nevada
        Wyoming
        California

3 Where is Mount Etna?
Is it:
        On the Italian coast near Naples
        In Chile
        On Crete
        On Sicily

4 What is the name of the mountain range which acts as a physical boundary between Europe and Asia?

Is it:

    The Caucasus
    The Harz
    The Karakorum
    The Urals

5 Which is the highest mountain in West Germany?
Is it:

    The Jungfrau
    The Matterhorn
    The Zugspitze
    The Eiger

6 Who led the British expedition which made the first succesful ascent of the south-west face of Mount Everest?
Was it:

    Sir Edmund Hillary
    Doug Scott
    Dougal Haston
    Chris Bonington

7 La Paz is 3631 m (11,916 ft) above sea level and the highest capital city in the world. Of which country is it capital?
Is it:

    Ethiopia
    Bolivia
    Chile
    Yucatán

8 Which is the highest building in New York?
Is it:

    The World Trade Centre
    The Pan American Building
    The Empire State Building
    The Pentagon

9 What was the tallest building in the ancient world?
Was it:

    The mausoleum of Mausoleus

The Parthenon in Athens
The Pyramid of Cheops
The Hanging Gardens of Babylon

10 What animals did Hannibal lead over the Alps for the first time?
Were they:

      Donkeys
      Llamas
      Camels
      Elephants

IO

Numbers

1 How many fiddlers did Old King Cole have?
Were there:
>   Seven
>   A hundred
>   Twenty-two
>   Three

2 What is a 'score'?
Is it:
>   Twelve
>   Twenty
>   A hundred
>   Sixty

3 What is the number of the current Republic governing in France?
Is it:
>   The second
>   The ninth
>   The fifth
>   The first

4 If you dial 192 on a British telephone whom will you contact?
Is it:
>   The operator

Directory enquiries
The cricket score
New Scotland Yard

5 Who lives in No 11 Downing Street?
Is it:

The Foreign Secretary
The Prime Minister's Secretary
The French Ambassador
The Chancellor of the Exchequer

6 How many sides has a dodecagon?
Are there:

Twenty
Two hundred
Twelve
Fifteen

7 When people talk about the 'roaring forties' to what are
they referring?
Is it:

A stormy area of the ocean
The Second World War
Jane Mansfield's bust
Ali Baba's thieves

8 What is the line of latitude dividing Canada from the
U.S.A?
Is it:

The Tropic of Capricorn
The 60th parallel
The 49th parallel
The 38th parallel

9 How many days did the Arab-Israeli war of 1967 last?
Was it:

Five days
Two days
Three weeks
Six days

10 Although the Third Reich only lasted for twelve years, for how long did Adolf Hitler promise it would last? For:

        Twenty years
        A hundred years
        A thousand years
        Eternity

II

Eureka!

1 Who invented television?
Was it:

>Albert Einstein
>Sir Frank Whittle
>John Logie Baird
>Thomas Alva Edison

2 He invented screw-propulsion, sluice-gates, swimming-belts and scissors. Who was he?
Was it:

>Leonardo da Vinci
>Galileo Galilei
>Sir Humphrey Davy
>Sir Walter Raleigh

3 What happens when you put sodium chloride into a glass of water?
Does it:

>Turn the water green
>Froth and bubble over the top
>Dissolve and make the water taste salty
>Dissolve and make the water taste sweet

4 When light is passed through a prism what colour does it disperse into apart from red, orange, yellow, green, blue and indigo?

Is it:

        Violet
        Magenta
        Cerise
        Aquamarine

5 Whose idea led to the development of postage stamps in Britain in 1840?
Was it:

        Lord North
        Anthony Trollope
        Sir Rowland Hill
        William Ewart Gladstone

6 Which branch of mathematical calculation was devised by Sir Isaac Newton in the middle of the seventeenth century?
Was it:

        Algebra
        The binary system
        Trigonometry
        Calculus

7 What everyday household activity inspired James Watt to invent the steam engine?
Was it:

        Doing the washing-up
        Boiling a kettle
        Having a bath
        Pumping water by hand

8 Which was the aircraft designed by Sir Christopher Cockerell?
Was it:

        The autogyro
        The airship
        The helicopter
        The hovercraft

9 What prize do we connect with the inventor of dynamite? Is it:

> The Queen's Award to Industry
> The William Hardcastle Prize
> The Nobel Prize
> The Whittaker Prize

10 Which famous British inventor designed both the Wellington bomber and the 'bouncing bomb'? Was it:

> Sir Barnes Wallis
> Guy Gibson
> 'Bomber' Harris
> Sir Ralph Cochrane

12

Olympic Games

1 In which alpine resort were the first Winter Olympics held in 1924?
Was it:

        Zermatt
        Chamonix
        Grenoble
        Innsbruck

2 Where in Greece were the ancient Olympic Games held?
Was it:

        At the base of Mount Olympus
        At Marathon
        At Thebes
        At Olympia

3 Nadia Comaneci was only fourteen when she won a gold medal for gymnastics in the 1976 Montreal Olympics. What nationality is she?
Is it:

        Bulgarian
        Russian
        Romanian
        Yugoslavian

4 What is the name of the American swimmer who won seven gold medals at the 1972 Olympics?

Is it:

Geoff Capes
Mark Spitz
David Wilkie
Mary Peters

5 In which European capital were the first modern **Olympic** Games held in 1896, at the instigation of Baron de Coubertin? Was it:

Stockholm
Paris
Athens
Rome

6 Which male high jumper originated a unique style of jump, that enabled him to rise from forty-eighth in the world in 1967 to Olympic champion the following year? Is it:

Richard Meade
David Hemery
Richard Fosbury
Cyril Fletcher

7 What is the name of the remarkable film of the 1964 Olympics? Is it:

White Rock
Tokyo Olympiad
The Games
Olympische Spiele

8 The 1980 Olympic Games will be held in Moscow, **but** where will the Winter Olympics be held that year? Is it:

Leningrad
St Moritz
Lake Placid
Denver

9 How many summer events are there in the current Olympic schedule?
Are there:

        Thirty
        Twenty-one
        Fifty
        Seventeen

10 Four successive Olympic Games have been held in cities beginning with 'M'. The last three names are Munich, Montreal and Moscow (the latter venue has been allocated the 1980 Games), but which is the first name?
Is it:

        Madrid
        Milan
        Mexico City
        Melbourne

13

-ologies and -isms

1 What is egotism?
Is it:

An insatiable desire to eat omelettes
Strong self-interest and self-admiration
The scientific name for 'work'
A form of Latin poetry

2 What is histology?
Is it:

The study of organic tissues
The academic discipline of writing history books
The study of snakes
The study of butterflies

3 What does a hydrologist do?
Does he:

Manufacture H-bombs
Build airships
Find water and control its distribution
Manufacture and develop hydraulic equipment

4 Which of these famous artists practised Cubism for part of his artistic career?
Was it:

> Michelangelo
> Vincent Van Gogh
> Claude Monet
> Pablo Picasso

5 What is an analogy?
Is it:

> A skin rash
> A direction in a musical score
> A similarity
> An irregular verb

6 If you practised stoicism what would you do?
Would you:

> Eat, drink and be merry with total abandon
> Sit cross-legged and chant for hours
> Abstain from pleasure
> Only eat meat

7 A malapropism is named after a character in which English play?
Is it:

> George Bernard Shaw's *Man and Superman*
> William Shakespeare's *Richard III*
> Richard Sheridan's *The Rivals*
> Sir Arthur Wing Pinero's *Trelawny of the Wells*

8 What is Taoism?
Is it:

> An oriental philosophy and religion
> A twentieth-century art form
> The study of evolution
> A technique for removing unwanted body hair

9 Which Scottish king wrote a book entitled *Daemonologie* in 1559?

Was it:

     Malcolm I
     Duncan
     Macbeth
     James VI

10 How many works of art would you expect to find in a tetralogy?

Are there:

     Thirteen
     Thirty
     Four
     Three

14

Land-marks

1 Where would you expect to see the Sugar Loaf mountain?
Is it:

> At Cape Town
> In the Himalayas
> At Rio de Janeiro
> At Gibraltar

2 What is the name of the Cathedral of Rome?
Is it:

> St Mark's
> St John Lateran
> St Peter's
> St Augustine's

3 The Statue of Liberty stands at the entrance to which American port?
Is it:

> Boston
> San Francisco
> New York
> Chicago

4 The Taj Mahal stands on the banks of the River Jumna in which Indian city?
Is it:

> Agra

Delhi
Benares
Calcutta

5 What is the most southerly point of the mainland of Great Britain?
Is it:

Lizard Point
Land's End
Portland Bill ·
Beachy Head

6 Where is the Bridge of Sighs?
Is it:

In Florence
In Venice
In Amsterdam
In Copenhagen

7 Stonehenge is the name of a famous group of standing stones in Wiltshire; what is the name of another group in Brittany?
Is it:

Padirac
Rocamadour
Carnac
Liège

8 Where is Tierra del Fuego?
Is it:

In Mexico
The name for Gibraltar in Spanish
In Indonesia
At the extreme south of South America

9 For what is Pisa most famous?
Is it:

> The cathedral
> The town hall
> The leaning tower
> The Sistine chapel

10 What is the deepest natural depression on earth?
Is it:

> The Great Rift Valley
> The Dead Sea
> The Sea of Galilee
> The Grand Canyon

15

Man and Wife

1 Who was Henry VIII's third wife?
Was she:

        Catherine Howard
        Jane Parr
        Catherine of Aragon
        Jane Seymour

2 What was the Duchess of Windsor called before she married the Duke of Windsor?
Was she:

        Lady Caroline Lamb
        Mrs Ernest Simpson
        Lillie Langtry
        Lady Diana Cooper

3 Which American actress is married to Paul Newman?
Is it:

        Joanne Woodward
        Natalie Wood
        Raquel Welch
        Liza Minelli

4 Marie Antoinette was one of the queens of France. Who was her husband?
Was it:

> Louis XIV, the Sun King
> Henry V
> Napoleon Bonaparte
> Louis XVI

5 Which nineteenth-century poet did Elizabeth Barrett marry?
Was it:

> William Wordsworth
> Robert Browning
> Robert Southey
> Alfred, Lord Tennyson

6 In William Shakespeare's play *The Merchant of Venice* whom does Portia marry?
Is it:

> Antonio
> Shylock
> Lorenzo
> Bassanio

7 To whom was the British Ambassador in the United States from 1977–9 married?
Was it:

> Mary Callaghan
> Elizabeth Taylor
> The Duchess of Gloucester
> Mary Wilson

8 Who was Humphrey Bogart's last wife, who outlives him?
Is she:

> Ann Todd
> Jean Harlow
> Lauren Bacall
> Ingrid Bergman

9 Who was Queen Anne's husband?
Was it:

> George I
> The Young Pretender
> Alexander Pope
> George, Prince of Denmark

10 Whom did Ryan O'Neal marry in *Love Story*?
Was it:

> Faye Dunaway
> Ali McGraw
> Liza Minelli
> Jane Fonda

16

Fractions

1 It is surprising to think that a quarter of the world's forests are located in one country, but which country is it?
Is it:

        Brazil
        Canada
        U.S.S.R.
        China

2 What is 0.125 as a fraction?
Is it:

        A quarter
        An eighth
        Two-fifths
        Three-sixteenths

3 How much of the earth's surface is covered by sea?
Is it:

        Three-quarters
        Two-thirds
        Five-sevenths
        Half

4 Where would you expect to find a quarter of the world's cattle population?
Is it:

        In Argentina
        In the U.S.A.

In Australia
In India

5 What is the prefix meaning one millionth part?
Is it:

Mega-
Micro-
Milli-
Mini-

6 What was Tennyson describing in these lines: 'Half a league, half a league,/ Half a league onward'?
Was it:

The University Boat Race
The Charge of the Light Brigade
The maiden voyage of the *Great Eastern*
The construction of the Manchester Ship Canal

7 How much of the human brain is water?
Is it:

One third
Half
Four-fifths
Three-quarters

8 What do we call the measurement for an eighth of a mile?
Is it:

A fathom
An acre
A furlong
A chain

9 When a man talks about his 'better half' to what is he referring?
Is it:

His wife
His mother
The lower part of his body
The side of his body on which he writes

53

10 What is the geometrical name for half of a diameter?
Is it:

A semiameter
A tangent
A radius
A circumference

17

Death and Disaster

1 What is the name of the Welsh mining village where 116 children and 28 adults were killed in a landslide in 1966? Is it:

> Merthyr Tydfil
> Abergavenny
> Aberfan
> Builth Wells

2 Which Secretary-General of the United Nations was killed in a plane crash in 1960? Was it:

> Trygve Lie
> U Thant
> Dean Rusk
> Dag Hammerskjöld

3 What famous disaster hit London in 1666? Was it:

> The Great Fire
> The Civil War
> The flooding of the river Thames
> The Great Plague

4 Who died in his bath?
Was it:

>Jean-Paul Marat
>Agamemnon
>Jean-Paul Sartre
>Casanova

5 Where in London is Poets' Corner?
Is it:

>In St Paul's Cathedral
>In Parliament Square
>In Westminster Abbey
>In the British Library

6 Which European capital was severely affected by an earthquake in March 1977?
Was it:

>Prague
>Ankara
>Sofia
>Bucharest

7 What ancient city was destroyed and engulfed by lava from the eruption of Mount Vesuvius in A.D. 79?
Was it:

>Carthage
>Corinth
>Pompeii
>Ephesus

8 Who shot Lee Harvey Oswald in 1963?
Was it:

>Lyndon Johnson
>Jack Ruby
>Bugsy Malone
>John Glenn

9 What is the colour of mourning in most Moslem countries?
Is it:

>Yellow

Violet
Black
White

10 What disaster killed one person in four in Europe during the fourteenth century?
Was it:

      The Thirty Years' War
      The Black Death
      The Wars of the Roses
      The War of Jenkins' Ear

18

World Cities

1 Which was the largest city in the world until 1957?
Was it:

       New York
       Shanghai
       London
       Tokyo

2 Quito is the capital of which country in the Western hemisphere?
Is it:

       Ecuador
       Guatemala
       Peru
       Uruguay

3 Which is the oldest inhabited city in the world?
Is it:

       Jerusalem
       Peking
       Damascus
       Istanbul

4 Which American city is named after an ancient capital of Egypt?
Is it:

       Wichita

Phoenix
Minneapolis
Memphis

5 Where is the city of Wellington?
Is it:

On the North Island of New Zealand
On the South Island of New Zealand
On the island of Tasmania
In Papua New Guinea

6 What was the former name of Ho Chi Minh City?
Was it:

Hanoi
Phnom Penh
Saigon
Manila

7 Into which North American city was Concorde first allowed access to fly scheduled flights?
Was it:

Boston
New York
Quebec
Washington

8 Which is the oldest university city in Europe?
Is it:

Paris
Parma
Padua
Pavia

9 In which British city is *The Prime of Miss Jean Brodie* set?
Is it:

Cheltenham
Edinburgh
Cambridge
York

10 The first atom bomb was dropped on Hiroshima; where was the second one dropped?
Was it:

> Nagoya
> Nagasaki
> Kyoto
> Osaka

19

Crime and Punishment

1 For what crime was Oscar Wilde imprisoned in 1895?
Was it:

> Libel
> Slander
> 'Acts of gross indecency'
> Indeecnt exposure

2 Which notorious murderer does Richard Attenborough portray in the film *Ten Rillington Place*?
Is it:

> James Hanratty
> John Christie
> Jack the Ripper
> The Boston Strangler

3 Of what crime is William Shakespeare generally believed to have been guilty?
Is it:

> Infringement of copyright
> Poaching
> Directing plays during the Commonwealth period
> Piracy

4 What historical event led to the sitting of the 'Bloody Assize'?
Was it:

> The Battle of Culloden Moor
> The Peasants' Revolt
> The Civil War
> The Battle of Sedgemoor

5 Who is the international criminal constantly pursued across the cinema screen by James Bond and who was responsible for the murder of Bond's wife in *On Her Majesty's Secret Service*?
Is it:

> Dr No
> Blofeld
> Thrush
> Goldfinger

6 Where in London is the Chamber of Horrors?
Is it:

> In the Tower of London
> In the Houses of Parliament
> In Madame Tussaud's
> In Oxford Street

7 Who or what is Alcatraz?
Is it:

> A prison in San Francisco Bay
> One of the Watergate burglars
> The Brazilian secret police
> The town where Benito Mussolini was executed

8 Where was the French penal colony called Devil's Island, which featured prominently in the story of Papillon?
Was it:

> In French West Africa
> In Cambodia
> In French Guiana
> Off the south coast of Corsica

62

9 What was the name of the famous nineteenth-century criminal played by Mick Jagger in the film of the same name? Was it:

> Pat Garrett
> Billy the Kid
> Ned Kelly
> Butch Cassidy

10 Which Russian novelist wrote *Crime and Punishment*? Was it:

> Ivan Turgenyev
> Fyodor Mikhailovich Dostoevsky
> Maxim Gorky
> Count Leo Nikolaievich Tolstoy

20

Initials

1 What do the initials R.A.E. represent?
Is it:

> Royal Automobile Engines
> Racing Aircraft Entries
> Rear Admiral's Ensign
> Royal Aircraft Establishment

2 What is the P.L.P.?
Is it:

> The Palestine Liberation Pact
> The Portuguese Liberal Parliament
> Pakistan Liquor Prohibition
> The Parliamentary Labour Party

3 What does A.R.C. stand for?
Is it:

> American Reactor Control
> Association of Registered Clowns
> Agricultural Research Council
> Agent of Russian Communism

4 What is C.A.R.D.?
Is it:

> The Campaign Against Racial Discrimination
> The Central Authority for Rural Development

The Criminals' Advice and Rehabilitation Department

Civil Aviation Regional Director

5 What is the I.R.B.M.?
Is it:

The Inland Rivers Board of Maintenance
Irish Religious Brethren Movement
Intermediate-range ballistic missile
The Inner Ring of Band Masters

6 What does O.C.A.S. mean?
Is it:

Oxford and Cambridge Arts Society
Official of the Central Air Security
Ordinary Common and Small
Organization of Central American States

7 What does I.M.S. mean?
Is it:

Instant mashed spinach
Inter-Governmental Marine Society
Indian Medical Service
International Monetary Securities

8 What is an F.R.C.O.?
Is he:

A Fellow of the Regional Crafts Organization
A Free Range Consultant Opthalmist
A Fellow of the Royal College of Organists
A Fellow of the Royal College of Obstetricians

9 What does C.C.P.R. stand for?
Is it:

Central Council for Physical Recreation
Central Committee of the Polish Republic
County Council Private Road
Canadian Council for the Preservation of Reindeer

10 What is the D.E.S.?
Is it:

        The Directorate of Episcopal Societies
        The Department of Education and Science
        Diploma in Equine Surgery
        Degree in Earth Sciences

21

Book-worm

1 Which black American author wrote the novel *Roots* that became the popular television serial?
Was it:

> John Steinbeck
> Martin Luther King
> Alex Haley
> Andrew Young

2 Which German politician wrote *Mein Kampf* (*My Struggle*)?
Was it:

> Adolf Hitler
> Prince Otto von Bismarck
> Helmut Schmidt
> Hermann Goering

3 The television series *All Creatures Great and Small* is based on the stories by which English writer?
Is it:

> Walter de la Mare
> Somerset Maugham
> James Herriot
> Arthur Scargill

4 Which American author wrote the chilling novel that led to the film *Jaws*?
Is it:

>William Faulkner
>Peter Bentley
>Edgar Allan Poe
>Peter Benchley

5 Where is the *Encyclopaedia Britannica* based and published?
Is it:

>In Chicago
>In Edinburgh
>In London
>In New York

6 Which English novelist wrote *Far From the Madding Crowd*?
Was it:

>Charles Dickens
>Henry James
>Daphne du Maurier
>Thomas Hardy

7 What nationality was Joseph Conrad, author of *Lord Jim, The Nigger of the Narcissus* and *The Rescue*?
Was he:

>Polish
>Canadian
>Dutch
>American

8 Who was Dr Johnson's biographer?
Was it:

>John Dryden
>Oliver Goldsmith
>James Boswell
>Henry Fielding

9 Samuel Pepys was one of the greatest seventeenth-century English diarists; who is the other one often ranked with him?

Is it:

>Izaak Walton
>John Evelyn
>Matthew Arnold
>Thomas de Quincey

10 What is the title of the play written by the Nobel Prize winning Russian novelist Alexander Solzhenitsyn?
Is it:

>*Cancer Ward*
>*The First Circle*
>*The Love Girl and The Innocent*
>*The Gulag Archipelago*

22

Figures of Speech

1 What is an 'oxymoron'?
Is it:

> The use of contradictory words in a single statement
> An idiotic statement
> The name of a part when you mean the complete object or idea
> An untranslatable word or phrase

2 What is a 'meiosis'?
Is it:

> A manner of speaking where the speaker is constantly preoccupied with himself
> A continuation of an idea mentioned sometime previously and forgotten by the reader or listener
> A general understatement
> A hesitant manner of speaking

3 What is 'hyperbole'?
Is it:

> Indirect or reported speech
> A condensed simile
> The use of a feigned sanctity to describe lewd behaviour
> The use of exaggeration for terms of emphasis

4 What is a 'pathetic fallacy'?

Is it:

> A ridiculous idea
> A guess
> The assumption that natural things have feelings like human beings
> An attempt by a speaker to cover an obvious error in his speech

5 What is 'alliteration'?
Is it:

> The use of words that repeat the same consonant
> The use of words that repeat the same vowel
> The style of writing which takes the form of a letter
> Writing or speech frequently interspersed with literary allusions

6 What is 'innuendo'?
Is it:

> The rearrangement of letters in a word to form another word
> A form of rhythmical cadence
> A hint or a suggestion
> A deliberate understatement

7 What is 'onomatopoeia'?
Is it:

> A severe case of 'verbal diarrhoea'
> The use of words which reproduce or echo the sounds they suggest
> The subtle use of abuse
> Likening two opposite things

8 What is an 'epigram'?
Is it:

> A sharp, memorable quip or saying
> The words on a tombstone in elegiac form
> A word inserted between the two parts of an infinitive
> A form of extended pun

9 What is 'bathos'?
Is it:

> An inaccuracy in vocabulary
> The conclusion of a literary idea
> The descent from lofty to trivial things
> The use of complicated words to express simple ideas

10 What is a 'tautology'?
Is it:

> The constant use of platitudes
> Unnecessary repetition
> A word with a similar sound to another word but with the opposite meaning
> A word with more than one meaning applicable in any particular use

23

Cheers!

1 What do the initials V.S.O.P. stand for on a bottle of brandy?

Is it:

> Very Special Old Pale
> Vin Spécial, Offre Publique
> Very Special Old Plonk
> Vin Supérieur Originé de Paris

2 Who was Dom Pérignon?

Was he:

> The cellar man to Louis XIV
> The blind monk who first invented champagne
> The first managing director of Moet et Chandon
> The monk who developed Benedictine

3 Which ancient general lends his name to a cocktail made from *crème de cacao*, cream and gin or brandy?

Is it:

> Pompey
> Hannibal
> Wallbanger
> Alexander

4 Where does the wine we call sherry come from?
Is it:

        The town of Sherrias in Portugal
        The town of Jerez in Spain
        From the Sharif region of Algeria
        From the town of Sherry in South Africa

5 Who was drowned in a butt of malmsey?
Was it:

        Leonardo da Vinci
        The little princes in the Tower of London
        The Duke of Clarence, brother of Richard III
        Nell Gwyn

6 What soft fruit is used to make the French liqueur *crème de cassis*?
Is it:

        Raspberries
        Plums
        Blackcurrants
        Strawberries

7 What is 'black velvet'?
Is it:

        A mixture of coffee and brandy
        A mixture of Guinness and champagne
        A brand of continental lager
        That part of the hangover before the headache sets in

8 For what chemical is tonic water particularly noted?
Is it:

        Iodine
        Quinine
        Sodium
        Camphor

9 What is the name of the drink which goes cloudy when water is added?

Is it:

> Pernod
> Ricard
> Ouzo
> Raki

10 Beer is flavoured with hops, wine is made from grapes but what is whisky made from?
Is it:

> Oats
> Rye
> Barley
> Millet

24

World Alliances

1 Which independent sovereign state in Europe does not belong to the United Nations, apart from the Holy See?
Is it:

> Sweden
> Ireland
> West Germany
> Switzerland

2 What is C.O.M.E.C.O.N.?
Is it:

> The international communications organization
> A 'mafia' for specialists in fraud and deception
> The Communist counterpart of the European Community
> A free-church union

3 Which country withdrew from the Commonwealth in January 1972?
Was it:

> Uganda
> Pakistan
> Sri Lanka (Ceylon)
> Malta

4 Which European country withdrew its forces from N.A.T.O. in 1975?

Was it:
>
> France
> Yugoslavia
> Greece
> Luxembourg

5 What nationality is Dr Kurt Waldheim, the U.N. Secretary-General, who was elected to the office in 1972? Is he:
>
> German
> American
> Austrian
> Danish

6 How many members are there of the Warsaw Pact? Are there:
>
> Seven
> Nine
> Twelve
> Five

7 The Lomé Convention is part of which international grouping? Is it:
>
> The Organization of African Unity
> The Colombo Plan
> The European Economic Community
> The Rio Pact

8 What area of the world is the A.N.Z.U.S. treaty intended to shield? Is it:
>
> The Arctic
> The Antarctic
> The Middle East
> Australasia

9 Which of the Axis powers in the Second World War had been on the same side as the Allies during the First World War?

Was it:

> Turkey
> Japan
> Italy
> Iran

10 Great Britain, Iran and Pakistan are three of the members of C.E.N.T.O.; which country is the fourth?

Is it:

> India
> Afghanistan
> Turkey
> Iraq

25

Streets Ahead

1 What is Fleet Street in London named after?
Is it:

> A prison
> A river
> The Royal Navy
> The first English newspaper

2 Sir James Barrie wrote a sentimental comedy with a street name for its title. What is it called?
Is it:

> *The Barretts of Wimpole Street*
> *Princes Street*
> *Quality Street*
> *The Streets of Life*

3 Where did Molly Malone push 'her wheelbarrow through the streets broad and narrow'?
Was it:

> In Dublin
> In Liverpool
> In Dundee
> In Belfast

4 Which playwright wrote *A Streetcar Named Desire*?
Was it:

> Edward Albee
> Tennessee Williams

J. D. Salinger
Arthur Miller

5 Which of the roads built by the Romans in Britain ran between London and York?
Was it:

        Antonine Street
        Watling Street
        Akeman Street
        Ermine Street

6 What was Grub Street famous for in eighteenth-century London?
Was it:

        Restaurants
        Hack writers
        Fleas and lice
        St Grub's Church

7 Which folk-singer wrote and sings 'The Streets of London'?
Is it:

        Donovan
        Bob Dylan
        Ralph McTell
        Paul Simon

8 Which London street is named after a famous eighteenth-century actor?
Is it:

        Garrick Street
        Curzon Street
        Harley Street
        Baker Street

9 Which European artist painted the *Street in Auvers* in 1890?
Was it:

        Édouard Manet
        Paul Cézanne
        Vincent Van Gogh
        Toulouse-Lautrec?

10 What did the 1959 Street Offences Act aim to achieve? Was it:

To prohibit the sounding of car horns after 11.30 p.m.

To remove prostitution from the streets

To make the use of side-lights obligatory at night

To ban the sale of hot-dogs on Sundays

26

Funny Ha Ha

1 What is the name of the famous police force that features in many silent comedies?
Is it:

> The Beverly Hills Bobbies
> The Keystone Cops
> The Broadway Runners
> The Hollywood Ten

2 Which of the following comedians starred in the 1940 film *A Chump at Oxford*?
Was it:

> Stan Laurel
> Charlie Chaplin
> Buster Keaton
> Oliver Hardy

3 Which British comedian played the part of the grave-digger in the 1948 film of *Hamlet*?
Was it:

> Stanley Holloway
> Jack Hulbert
> Richard Murdoch
> Bud Flanagan

4 Two of the Marx brothers left the act. One of them was Gummo, who was the other?

Was it:
> Groucho
> Chico
> Zeppo
> Harpo

5 What is the title of the first of the Ealing comedies?
Is it:
> *The Lavender Hill Mob*
> *Passport to Pimlico*
> *Hello London*
> *Jumping for Joy*

6 Which American comedian, best known for his television and radio work, won an Oscar for his performance in *The Sunshine Boys*?
Was it:
> Walter Matthau
> Dick Van Dyke
> George Burns
> Phil Silvers

7 What is the Pink Panther, in the film of the same name?
Is it:
> An international thief
> A priceless gem
> A holiday hotel
> A police code name for Inspector Clouseau

8 Which was the first of the *Carry On* films?
Was it:
> *Carry On Cleo*
> *Carry On Screaming*
> *Carry On Sergeant*
> *Carry On Nurse*

9 Who was the actress who played opposite Tony Hancock in many of his *Hancock's Half Hour* radio programmes?
Was it:

Joan Sims
Hattie Jacques
Cicely Courtneidge
Glenda Farrell

10 Who conceived the school full of female horrors called St Trinians?
Was it:

Alistair Sim
Peter Sellers
Spike Milligan
Ronald Searle

27

Resident Aliens

1 What does *à la carte* mean in a restaurant?
Is it:

       Served from the trolley
       According to the menu
       Service not included
       Cover charge

2 If you commit a *faux pas* what do you do?
Do you:

       Cross a road without using a zebra-crossing
       Make a tactless comment
       Put different coloured socks on either foot
       Kick someone's pet

3 *Ich dien* ('I serve') is the motto of whom?
Is it:

       The Order of the Bath
       The Prince of Wales
       The Order of the Garter
       The holders of the O.B.E.

4 What does *in vino veritas* mean?
Is it:

       There is a worm in my wine
       A drunken man speaks the truth

This is real wine
A day without wine is like a day without sunshine

5 What is a *coup de théâtre*?
Is it:

A striking theatrical effect
A feigned blow used by actors in stage fighting
A change of artistic director
A dazzling box-office success

6 What are *belles lettres*?
Are they:

Attractive handwriting
Love letters
Essays or poems
Key signatures on musical scores

7 What is a *bête noire*?
Is it:

A black sheep
A form of gambling
A special object of dislike
An I.O.U.

8 If you are advised to *carpe diem* what should you do?
Would you:

Make good use of the present
Kill time
Tell the truth
Praise God

9 If you have an *embarras de richesses* in what situation do you find yourself?
Are you:

Overtaxed because of your wealth
Intellectually gifted
Having difficulty in choosing with so much to choose from
A member of an aristocratic family

10 *Per ardua ad astra* is the motto of which organization? Is it:

> The Royal Marines
> The United States Marine Corps
> The National Coal Board
> The Royal Air Force

28

Nature Trail

1 What is the largest animal without a backbone?
Is it:

        The giant squid
        The giant tortoise
        The python
        The anaconda

2 Which is the fastest mammal on earth over short distances?
Is it:

        The leopard
        The kangaroo
        The cheetah
        The antelope

3 What is the largest type of whale?
Is it:

        The sperm whale
        The killer whale
        The pilot whale
        The blue whale

4 What is characteristic about marsupials?
Do they:

        Stand on their hind legs
        Carry their young in pouches

Hibernate
Drink sea-water

5 What is the more common name for the *canis familiaris*?
Is it:

    The domestic cat
    The domestic dog
    The horse
    The chicken

6 What is a smolt?
Is it:

    A collective name for a group of sparrows
    A young salmon
    A young zebra
    The period when an animal's coat grows to its full
    length

7 What was the name of the famous gorilla who lived in the
London Zoo?
Was it:

    George
    Garfield
    Guy
    Gus

8 Which living bird has the longest wing-span?
Is it:

    The golden eagle
    The condor
    The albatross
    The harpy eagle

9 Where on a fish would you find the dorsal fin?
Is it:

    The tail
    Attached to its belly
    On its back
    Just behind its gills

10 Which is the world's fastest running bird?
Is it:

        The ostrich
        ·The emu
        The dodo
        The domestic chicken

29

Number One

1 Who made the first non-stop transatlantic crossing by aeroplane?
Was it:

        Amy Johnson
        Charles Lindbergh
        Alcock and Brown
        Richard Byrd

2 What is the title of the first full-length film made by the Beatles?
Is it:

        Ferry 'Cross The Mersey
        Help
        Magical Mystery Tour
        A Hard Day's Night

3 Who was the first archbishop of Canterbury?
Was it:

        St Anselm
        St Augustine
        St Thomas Becket
        St Dunstan

4 What kind of slippers did the first Cinderella wear?
Were they:

        Gold
        White ermine

Glass
Diamond

5 Who was the first black football player to win a full England soccer cap?
Was it:

        Daley Thompson
        Basil d'Olivera
        Viv Anderson
        Nat King Cole

6 According to the song what did 'my true love' bring to me on the first day of Christmas?
Was it:

        A French hen
        A lily white boy
        A pheasant
        A partridge

7 What is the first Commandment?
Is it:

        'Thou shalt not kill'
        'Thou shalt not commit adultery'
        'Thou shalt have no other gods before me'
        'Thou shalt not make unto thee any graven image'

8 Which was the first British football club to win the European Cup Winner's Cup, in 1963?
Was it:

        Tottenham Hotspur
        Glasgow Rangers
        Manchester United
        Arsenal

9 What is the title of the first talking film?
Is it:

        Gone With The Wind
        The Jazz Singer

The Wizard of Oz
Citizen Kane

10 Which was the first city in Normandy liberated by the Allies in 1944?
Was it:

St Nazaire
Dieppe
Caen
Dunkirk

30

On Four Wheels

1 With what car component do you connect the name Hardy-Spicer?
Is it:

> The steering wheel
> Heaters
> Windscreen wipers
> Universal joints

2 What do the initials G.T. stand for on motor vehicles?
Is it:

> General Training
> Glamour Trim
> Grand Touring
> Greased Throughout

3 What feature(s) of a petrol engine is/are missing in a diesel engine?
Is it:

> A dynamo
> An oil pump
> A carburettor
> Sparking plugs

4 Where is the British Grand Prix held?
Is it:

At Brands Hatch
At Silverstone
At Oulton Park
At Brooklands

5 Who was the only racing driver to win the world championship driving his own cars?
Was it:

Alfa Romeo
Bruce McLaren
Jack Brabham
Ettore Bugatti

6 Which mass-produced car has had more models made than any other?
Is it:

The Volkswagen Beetle
The Citröen 2CV
The Austin-Morris Mini
The Fiat 500

7 What title did William Richard Morris take in 1934?
Was it:

Lord Morris
Sir William Morris
Lord Nuffield
Lord Austin

8 Which car currently holds the World Land Speed Record?
Is it:

'Blue Flame'
'Bluebird'
'Green Monster'
'Boyle Special'

9 What is the name of the great Argentinian racing driver who won the world championship five times and who retired in 1958?
Is it:

        Giusèppe Farina
        Alberto Ascari
        Juan-Manuel Fangio
        José-Froilan Gonzalez

10 What nationality is Mario Andretti?
Is he:

        American
        Portuguese
        Brazilian
        Italian

3 I

Composers

1 How many violin concertos did Beethoven write?
Was it:

> One
> Nine
> Six
> Three

2 Who composed *The Merry Widow*?
Was it:

> Johann Strauss
> Richard Heuberger
> Franz Lehár
> Emmerich Kalman

3 Which Russian composer wrote the ballet *The Firebird*?
Was it:

> Modest Mussorgsky
> Igor Stravinsky
> Mihail Glinka
> Pëtr Tchaikovsky

4 Which famous eighteenth-century composer wrote the
Farewell symphony?
Was it:

> Franz Joseph Haydn
> Wolfgang Amadeus Mozart

George Friedrich Handel
Johann Sebastian Bach

5 Who composed the score for *West Side Story*?
Was it:

George Gershwin
Leonard Bernstein
Aaron Copland
Cole Porter

6 What historical event was Tchaikovsky celebrating when he wrote the *1812 Overture*?
Was it:

The death of Nelson
The death of Napoleon
The Battle of Borodino
The Battle of Salamanca

7 Who wrote the play on which Mozart based his opera *The Marriage of Figaro*?
Was it:

Jean Racine
Pierre de Beaumarchais
Pierre Corneille
Victor Hugo

8 Which English composer wrote *The Dream of Gerontius*?
Was it:

Benjamin Britten
Sir Michael Tippett
Ralph Vaughan Williams
Sir Edward Elgar

9 Who wrote an overture about a cave on the island of Staffa?
Was it:

Frederick Delius
Edvard Grieg
Felix Mendelssohn
Henry Purcell

10 Who wrote the Christmas carol 'Hark The Herald Angels Sing'?
Was it:

John Wesley
Johann Sebastian Bach
John Henry Newman
John Fisher

32

Solid Foundations

1 Who lives at Chequers?
Is it:

        The Queen, while she is on holiday
        The Prime Minister
        The Speaker of the House of Commons
        The Lord Privy Seal

2 To where was London Bridge transported in 1970?
Was it:

        To Texas
        To Vancouver
        To Bath
        To Arizona

3 What is the name of the Cathedral of Paris?
Is it:

        St Michel
        St Jeanne
        Notre Dame
        St Elysée

4 What was the name of the German parliamentary assembly which was burnt down in 1933?
Was it:

        The Bundestag
        The Reichstag

The Rechtstag
The Deutsche Assemblie

5 Where is the Alhambra?
Is it:

In Morocco
In Saudi Arabia
In Spain
In Tunisia

6 What is the name of the famous archaeological site in southern Africa?
Is it:

Harrapa
Zimbabwe
Machu Picchu
Mohenjodaro

7 Which eighteenth-century playwright designed Castle Howard, in Yorkshire?
Was it:

William Congreve
Sir Richard Steele
Sir John Vanbrugh
Oliver Goldsmith

8 What is the name of the Minoan city on Crete which was excavated and partially reconstructed by Sir Arthur Evans?
Is it:

Mycenae
Phaestos
Mallia
Knossos

9 What was the Colossus at Rhodes, apart from being one of the seven wonders of the ancient world? Was it:

A lighthouse
A temple
A castle
A statue

10 What is the tallest building in Washington D.C.? Is it:

The White House
The Pentagon
The Capitol
The Library of Congress

33
Wham, Zap, Pow!

1 Who plays the part of Superman's father in the film *Superman*?
Is it:

James Mason
Marlon Brando
Ryan O'Neal
Dustin Hoffman

2 How many fingers has Mickey Mouse?
Is it:

Five
Six
Two
Four

3 What is the title of the satirical cartoon by Ralph Bashi made in 1971 set in the urban underground of contemporary America?
Is it:

Topcat
Fritz the Cat
The Last Picture Show
The Last Detail

4 Which was Walt Disney's first full-length cartoon?

Was it:

Fantasia
Pinocchio
Snow White and the Seven Dwarfs
The Sleeping Beauty

5 Who created Popeye?
Was it:

Max Fleischer
Pat Sullivan
Walter Lanz
Hanna-Barbera

6 From which planet did Superman originate?

Mars
Venus
Krypton
Andromeda

7 What was the name of Dan Dare's companion?
Was it:

Tubby
Algy
Bob
Robin

8 Who is the English aristocrat that forms part of the Thunderbirds team?
Is it:

Virgil
Lady Penelope
Lord Parker
Scott

9 Which was Walt Disney's first Silly Symphony?
Was it:

Flowers and Trees
Donald Duck
Skeleton Dance
Bambi

10 Who wrote the stories on which the cartoon film *Jungle Book* is based?
Was it:

   C. S. Lewis
   Rudyard Kipling
   Edgar Rice Burroughs
   Rider Haggard

34

All Together Now

1 Who founded the Quaker Movement?
Was it:

> Charles James Fox
> Martin Luther
> George Fox
> Brigham Young

2 What is the Middle Temple?
Is it:

> A branch of the Masonic Society
> A part of a synagogue
> One of the Inns of Court which admit law students
> The Official name of the Mormon temple in Kansas
> City

3 What is the Monday Club?
Is it:

> A society for members of the Conservative Party
> A nickname for the Cabinet
> The headquarters of the actor's union Equity
> An extreme left-wing group in the Labour Party

4 Who was the founder of the Boy Scout Movement?
Was it:

> Lord Macaulay
> W. E. Gladstone

Oscar Wilde
Lord Baden-Powell

5 Which literary characters sealed their unity with the words
'all for one and one for all'?
Was it:
>King Arthur's knights
>The Musketeers
>The Swiss family Robinson
>The pilgrims in the Canterbury Tales

6 The Shiites form one of the two principal sects in Islam:
who form the other?
Is it:
>The Caliphs
>The Korans
>The Sunnites
>The Muezzins

7 What was the name given to those who campaigned for
English social reform between 1836 and 1858?
Was it:
>The Fabians
>The Luddites
>The Tolpuddle Martyrs
>The Chartists

8 Who sailed with Jason to find the Golden Fleece?
Was it:
>The Argonauts
>The Myrmidons
>The Phoenicians
>The Janissaries

9 A 'harras' is a collective noun for which animals?
Is it:
>Pigs
>Wolves
>Horses
>Mules

10 For what are philanthropists renowned?
Is it:

> Collecting butterflies
> Collecting stamps
> Love and care for mankind
> Riotous and extravagant living

35

Energy

1 Which country has the highest oil production in the world?
Is it:

 Iran
 U.S.S.R.
 Saudi Arabia
 U.S.A.

2 What is one horse-power?
Is it:

 746 watts
 The power required to raise 550 lbs one foot in one second
 The amount of energy expended by one horse ploughing one furlong
 The amount of energy expended by one team of horses ploughing one acre

3 After which scientist is the unit of energy named?
Is it:

 Joule
 Newton
 Hertz
 Pascal

4 Which country is the highest producer of uranium?

Is it:

Niger
Canada
U.S.A.
Australia

5 When did the first North Sea oil flow directly from the British sector to the mainland?
Was it:

In 1970
In 1975
In 1973
In 1976

6 What source of power was used to drive the first car to exceed 60 mph in 1899 and establish a new world land speed record?
Was it:

Electricity
Steam
Diesel
Petrol

7 How old is the coal mined in Britain?
Is it:

500 – 600 million years old
270 – 300 million years old
7000 – 8000 million years old
125,000 – 130,000 million years old

8 What is the metric equivalent of 30 mpg?
Is it:

7.8 km/l
10.6 km/l
12.4 km/l
17.7 km/l

9 Which country is the world's largest producer of coal?
Is it:

U.S.S.R.
Poland

West Germany
U.S.A.

10 What alternative source of energy was used to power some motor vehicles during the Second World War?
Was it:

Paraffin
Methane Gas
Kerosene
Sodium Chloride

36

Plays and Players

1 Which Elizabethan dramatist wrote a play entitled *Edward II*?
Was it:

> Ben Jonson
> Thomas Kyd
> Samuel Johnson
> Christopher Marlowe

2 Robert Bolt's play *A Man For All Seasons* is the story of the fall of which Tudor politician?
Was it:

> Thomas Cromwell
> Cardinal Wolsey
> Thomas More
> Thomas Cranmer

3 Which South American revolutionary did David Essex play in the musical *Evita*?
Is it:

> Che Guevara
> Fidel Castro
> Simón Bolívar
> Atahuallpa

4 Bertolt Brecht wrote *The Threepenny Opera* with Kurt Weill in 1928, but which eighteenth-century English play did he base it on?

Was it:

> *The Way of The World*
> *The Beggar's Opera*
> *She Stoops to Conquer*
> *Mack O'the Knife*

5 Which English playwright can be said to have begun the vogue of kitchen-sink drama with his 1956 play *Look Back in Anger*?
Was it:

> Joe Orton
> Harold Pinter
> John Osborne
> Jimmy Orton

6 Which British actor has become famous for his portrayal of the French Detective Inspector Maigret?
Is it:

> Noel Davis
> Rupert Davies
> Claude Rains
> Peter Sellers

7 Dysart is the name of the child psychiatrist in Peter Shaffer's play *Equus*. Who plays this role in the film of the play?
Is it:

> Richard Burton
> Alec McCowen
> Leonard Rossiter
> Michael Jayston

8 What is the title of Sir Terence Rattigan's play about the career of T. E. Lawrence?
Is it:

> *Lawrence of Arabia*
> *Shaw*
> *The Seven Pillars of Wisdom*
> *Ross*

9 Who played Desdemona in the film of *Othello* opposite Sir Laurence Olivier in the title role?
Was it:

> Janet Suzman
> Helen Mirren
> Maggie Smith
> Rachel Heyhoe-Flint

10 In which of Shakespeare's plays does the character Ariel appear?
Is it:

> *A Midsummer Night's Dream*
> *The Tempest*
> *Measure for Measure*
> *Timon of Athens*

37

World at War

1 In which Indian city did the Indian Mutiny (First War of Independence) begin?
Was it:

        Delhi
        Meerut
        Cawnpore
        Lucknow

2 How many Crusades were there?
Were there:

        Seven
        Three
        Nine
        Five

3 What is the name given to the religious wars fought in Germany during the seventeenth century?
Is it:

        The Hundred Years' War
        The War of the Spanish Succession
        The Thirty Years' War
        The Holy War

4 During which war did the defence of Rorke's Drift take place in 1879?

Was it:

> The Ashanti War
> The First Boer War
> The First Afghan War
> The Zulu War

5 What is the name of Picasso's masterpiece which was inspired by the horrors of the blitz witnessed during the Spanish Civil War?
Is it:

> *Homage to Catalonia*
> *A Farewell to Arms*
> *Guernica*
> *España*

6 Britain once fought a war in Africa which lasted thirty-eight minutes. Against which country was this waged?
Was it:

> Egypt
> Zanzibar
> Madagascar
> Uganda

7 How long was the Hundred Years' War?
Was it:

> 110 years
> 98 years
> 100 years
> 115 years

8 When was the Opium War?
Was it:

> In 1900–1901
> In 1794–1803
> In 1839–1842

9 What was the name of the war fought between Britain and Spain in 1739–1741?

Was it:

> The Iberian War
> The War of Jenkins' Ear
> The War of the King of Spain's Beard
> The Second Spanish War

10 What is the title of the famous book written by Julius Caesar about his wars against the barbarians?
Is it:

> *The Civil War*
> *The Germanic Wars*
> *The Conquest of Britain*
> *The Gallic Wars*

38

Measure for Measure

1 For what purpose is a calorimeter used?
Is it:

> To measure gas inside a pressurized bottle
> To measure quantities of heat
> To calculate the number of calories in food
> To test the pressure in hot air balloons

2 How long is a fathom?
Is it:

> 6 feet
> 6 metres
> 10 feet
> 10 yards

3 How many kilograms are there in a metric ton (tonne)?
Are there:

> 100
> 1000
> 50
> 20

4 How many pounds are there in a hundredweight (1 cwt)?
Are there:

> 100
> 400

160
112

5 For what commodity is a hogshead the measure?
Is it:
    Barley
    Cement
    Beverages
    Pork

6 What is measured on the Richter Scale?
Is it:
    Musical tones
    The international gold reserves
    Tidal waves
    Earthquakes

7 How long is a nautical mile?
Is it:
    5280 ft
    6080 ft
    1760 ft
    5000 ft

8 What is the international measurement for crude oil?
Is it:
    A barrel
    A firkin
    A gallon (U.S.)
    An Allah

9 On the Beaufort Scale what does Force 10 signify?
Is it:
    A gentle breeze
    A hurricane
    A storm
    A whole gale

10 What is the weight of a quart of pure water?
Is it:

$1\frac{1}{4}$ lbs

1 kilogram

$2\frac{1}{2}$ lbs

10 lbs

39

Underground

1 What is the name of the underground in Paris?
Is it:

> Le Underground
> Le Métro
> Le Sousterrain
> Le Michelin

2 Which London Underground station was the scene of a serious accident in 1975?
Was it:

> Liverpool Street
> Moorgate
> New Cross
> Archway

3 Which is the busiest underground in the world?
Is it in:

> New York
> Chicago
> Tokyo
> London

4 Which is the most extensive underground in the world?
Is it:

> In Paris
> In London

In Stockholm
In San Francisco

5 Which was the first city to open a length of underground railway?
Was it:

        London
        Paris
        Boston
        Berlin

6 On the London Underground what is the eastern terminus of the District Line?
Is it:

        Cockfosters
        Ongar
        Upminster
        Ealing Broadway

7 If you got on a tube at Queensway in London and travelled for three stops west on the Central Line before getting out, where would you be?
Would you be:

        At the White City
        At Lancaster Gate
        At Shepherd's Bush
        At Holland Park

8 Which was the first underground electric railway in the world?
Was it:

        The City and South London Railway
        The Manhattan District Line
        The Bakerloo Line
        The Paris Central Line

9 What is unusual about the subways of Rome compared with those of London and Paris?

Is it:

        There are no 'no-smoking' cars
        There are no fixed fares
        There is no underground railway in the city centre
        There are no escalators

10 What is the name of the Underground line on which London Transport began work in February 1972?
Is it:

        The Victoria Line
        The Regency Line
        The Jubilee Line
        The Fleet Line

40

Floccinaucinihilipilification

1 What is the meaning of 'diurnal'?
Is it:

        An organ of digestion in mammals
        Part of a lathe
        Occupying a day
        A ship's log

2 What is the meaning of 'terraqueous'?
Is it:

        The ability to dissolve in water
        A type of glaze used on European porcelain
        A geological name for marshes
        Comprising both water and land

3 What is a 'reredos'?
Is it:

        A breed of buffalo
        An ornamental screen at the back of an altar
        An instrument for measuring the texture of meat
        A prison slang word for an 'easy job'

4 When a Scotsman talks about a 'pibroch' to what is he referring?

Is it:

A series of variations for the bagpipes
A thick vegetable soup
An article of clothing
The sheath in which he carries his skene

5 What is an 'interregnum'?
Is it:

An instrument for measuring the inner dimensions
of objects
One of the main arteries leading from the human
heart
The period between one king and his successor
An official messenger belonging to the royal
household

6 What do you do to something when you 'extrapolate' it?
Do you:

Winch it out of the ground with pulleys
Reinforce it with wooden stakes
Deliberately increase its size with force-feeding
Calculate it by using a series of other terms

7 What is a 'diphthong'?
Is it:

An instrument used for branding sheep
Part of a cat-o'-nine-tails
The combination of two adjacent vowels
A form of musical notation

8 What are you if people call you 'lugubrious'?
Are you:

Lively, active and fond of mixing with people
Mournful and gloomy
Overweight
Able to speak several foreign languages

9 What is a 'valetudinarian'?
Is it:

A servant training to become a butler
A formal lettter of dismissal
Someone who is preoccupied with their state of health
A song of parting and farewell

10 What is a 'mixen'?
Is it:

A dunghill
A female badger
A flighty young girl
A sail on board a ship

41

Sailor Beware

1 Who was the first man to sail solo round the world?
Was it:

Sir Francis Chichester
Robin Knox-Johnson
Joshua Slocum
Alain Colas

2 What was the name of the yacht in which Clare Francis made her solo Atlantic crossing in 1976?
Was it:

Chivers' Jelly
Robertson's Golly
Pen Duick IV
Felicity Ann

3 What did the Viking sailor Lief Ericson do?
Did he:

Discover Iceland
Discover Greenland
Discover America
Establish the monastery on Lindisfarne

4 What was the name of the ship in which Sir Francis Drake sailed round the world in 1577–80?
Was she:

> *The Nina*
> *The Pelican*
> *The Golden Hind*
> *The Elizabeth*

5 Which Portuguese navigator discovered the sea route to India via the Cape of Good Hope?
Was it:

> Henry the Navigator
> Ferdinand Magellan
> Vasco da Gama
> Sebastian del Cano

6 What is the name of the sailor and naval officer created by C. S. Forester and subsequently played by Gregory Peck in a film of the same name?
Is it:

> Lord Jim
> Horatio Havelock
> Ross Poldark
> Horatio Hornblower

7 Who was the Dutch admiral who is claimed to have swept the English from the sea during the middle of the seventeenth century?
Was it:

> Cornelius van Dreben
> Johannes van der Waals
> Maarten van Tromp
> Michel de Ruyter

8 What was the name of the German battleship sunk in a Norwegian fjord in November 1944?
Was it:

> The *Bismarck*
> The *Graf Spee*

The *Prinz Eugen*
The *Tirpitz*

9 Where did Nelson lose his eye?
Was it:

At Calvi
At the Battle of the Nile
At the Battle of Tenerife
At the Battle of Trafalgar

10 Christopher Columbus's flagship was called the *Santa Maria* and one of the others was the *Pinta*. What was the name of the third one?
Was it:

The *Dove (Columba)*
The *Niña*
The *Santa Julia*
The *San Miguel*

42

The Bible

1 What is the third book in the Old Testament?
Is it:

        Deuteronomy
        Numbers
        Joshua
        Leviticus

2 Which is the longest psalm?
Is it:

        Psalm 56
        Psalm 23
        Psalm 119
        Psalm 130

3 Who was put into 'an ark of bulrushes' and left floating on the river when he was a baby?
Was it:

        Joshua
        Moses
        Gideon
        Laban

4 Who was rewarded with the head of John the Baptist?
Was it:

        Bathsheba
        Herodias

Ruth
Salome

5 What is the last book of the New Testament?
Is it:

    Malachi
    Daniel
    The Acts of the Apostles
    Revelation

6 Which Old Testament figure wore a coat of many colours?
Was it:

    David
    Samuel
    Joseph
    Job

7 For what faculty was King Solomon renowned?
Was it:

    Great wealth
    His love for the Queen of Sheba
    Wisdom
    Swordsmanship

8 What was the name of Samson's father?
Was it:

    Micah
    Joab
    Eli
    Manoah

9 Who was raised from the dead?
Was it:

    Elijah
    Elisha
    Lazarus
    Bartimaeus

10 Who was Barabbas?
Was he:

        The doubting apostle
        St Paul before his conversion
        The Roman soldier whose ear was cut off in the
        garden of Gethsemane
        The criminal who was released by Pontius Pilate
        in place of Jesus Christ

43

For Gallantry

1 The Victoria Cross is the first British decoration in order of precedence; what is the second?

Is it:

The Royal Red Cross
The George Cross
The Distinguished Service Cross
The Military Cross

2 Who was the American hero who rode from Boston to Lexington to warn the colonists of the British advance in 1775?

Was it:

Annie Oakley
George Washington
Paul Revere
Wyatt Earp

3 What was the name of the British boy hero who was awarded the Victoria Cross for his bravery at the battle of Jutland in 1916?

Was it:

John Cornwell
John Wilmot
Samuel Hood
Richard Nelson

4 Who was the hero king of Sparta that delayed the Persian advance into Greece at the battle of Thermopylae in 480 B.C.?
Was it:

        Spartacus
        Leonidas
        Xerxes
        Cyrus the Great

5 To whom was the Blue Max awarded?
Was it:

        American sailors
        German airmen
        German sailors
        South African infantry

6 Which British hero of the nineteenth century died at Lucknow?
Was it:

        Charles Gordon
        Sir William Napier
        Sir Henry Havelock
        Sir James Outram

7 What community was awarded the George Cross in 1942?
Was it:

        The citizens of Coventry
        The people of Singapore
        The inhabitants of Malta
        The inhabitants of Gibraltar

8 Which Roman hero held the bridge according to Lord Macaulay's poem named after him?
Was it:

        Lars Porsena
        Brutus
        Horatius
        Cassius

9 What is a posthumous award?
Is it:

> One that is awarded after the death of the person to whom it is presented
> One awarded out of humanitarian grounds
> One awarded by the monarch in person
> One awarded to a civilian while under the direct command of miltary or naval personnel

10 For what act of valour is the Albert Medal awarded?
Is it:

> For the saving of miners or quarrymen
> For the rescue of men wounded in military action
> For saving life at sea or on land
> For medical and nursing aid in battle

44

What's in a Name?

1 Which nineteenth-century novelist adopted the pen-name Mark Twain?
Was it:

>Samuel Clemens
>Abraham Lincoln
>Benjamin Disraeli
>Lord Byron

2 Vladimir Ilich Ulianov was the real name of which Russian politician?
Was it:

>Trotsky
>Lenin
>Stalin
>Khruschev

3 What was the former name of Surinam?
Was it:

>Bechuanaland
>Dutch Guiana
>Congo
>Nyasaland

4 Harry Houdini named himself after the French magician Houdin, but what was Houdini's real name?

>Charles Blondin

Lord Alfred Douglas
Ehrich Weiss
John Wilkes Booth

5 Who wrote under the pen-name of Saki?
Was it:

Alfred, Lord Tennyson
Charles Baudelaire
Walter de la Mare
Hector Hugh Munro

6 What title did Mr Quintin Hogg renounce?
Was it:

Earl of Sandwich
Viscount Stansgate
Viscount Hailsham
Earl of Durham

7 Who became the internationally acclaimed model Twiggy?
Was it:

Jean Shrimpton
Lesley Hornby
Jane Asher
Linda Jones

8 What would you be suffering from if your doctor diagnosed 'acute nasopharyngitis'?
Would it be:

A sore throat and a heavy cold
A hangover
A nose-bleed
Housemaid's knee

9 *First Impressions* was the original title of which of Jane Austen's novels?
Was it:

> *Mansfield Park*
> *Emma*
> *Pride and Prejudice*
> *Persuasion*

10 What was Lewis Carroll's real name?
Was it:

> Dean Liddell
> Charles Edward Carryl
> Arthur Joyce Cary
> Charles Lutwidge Dodgson

45

Space Travel

1 What was the name of the first manned spacecraft?
Was it:

> *Friendship I*
> *Vostok I*
> *Mercury I*
> *Sigma I*

2 Which Apollo spacecraft was the first to break free from
the earth's gravitational field and orbit the moon?
Was it:

> *Apollo V*
> *Apollo IX*
> *Apollo VIII*
> *Apollo III*

3 Who was the American president whose voice was first
heard on the surface of the moon?
Was it:

> John Kennedy
> Gerald Ford
> Richard Nixon
> Lyndon Johnson

4 Which planet did the American *Mariner IX* spacecraft orbit in 1971?

Was it:

        Mars
        Venus
        Jupiter
        Pluto

5 Vladimir Remek was the first non-Russian or non-American to fly in space in *Soyuz 28*. What nationality is he?

Is he:

        Polish
        Czech
        East German
        Hungarian

6 Where is the N.A.S.A. mission control centre?

Is it:

        In Washington D.C.
        At Cape Kennedy
        At Cape Canaveral
        In Houston

7 What was the name of the British rocket which was fired from the test site at Woomera, Australia?

Was it:

        Union Jack
        Blue Streak
        Britannia
        Red Devil

8 Who was the scientist whose research led to the development of space rockets?

Was it:

        Sir Bernard Lovell
        Dr Magnus Pyke
        Werner von Braun
        Patrick Moore

9 The American orbiting space station is called *Skylab*; what is the name of the Russian one?
Is it:

> *Voskhod*
> *Salyut*
> *Aurora*
> *Pioneer*

10 Neil Armstrong and Buzz Aldrin were two of the crew who made the first moon landing; who was the third member?
Was it:

> Alan Shepard
> James Lovell
> Eugene Cernan
> Michael Collins

46

Job Lot

1 What does an underwriter do?
Does he:

>Supervise the preparation and burial of the dead
>Deal in insurance
>Edit manuscripts
>Write the captions for cartoons and advertisements

2 What does a speleologist do?
Does he:

>Study the use of spelling
>Practise black magic
>Study and explore caves
>Keep a record of proceedings in a court of law

3 What does a lexicographer do?
Does he:

>Codify the law
>Compile dictionaries
>Take bets at sporting events
>Send messages by Morse code

4 What does Black Rod do?
Does he:

>Convey M.P.s to imprisonment in the Tower of London
>Act as an usher to the Lord Chamberlain's department

Administer the birch in the Isle of Man
Look after the dogs in the royal household

5 What is the name given to a man who makes his living
by collecting flotsam?
Is he:

     A beachcomber
     A longshoreman
     A docker
     A dustman

6 What does a purser do?
Does he:

     Make wallets
     Act as an official carrying money between banks
     Supervise the stocking and issue of provisions on
     board ship
     Track down missing persons

7 What does a stenographer do?
Does he:

     Design automatic weapons
     Act as a public orator
     Write in shorthand
     Produce stencils

8 What does a cartographer make?
Is it:

     Maps
     Transport vehicles
     Paper
     Legal documents

9 What did alchemists try to do?
Was it:

     To make gold out of base metals
     To find the secret of eternal youth
     To invent a means of making man fly
     To prove that the world was round

10 What does an orthodontist do?
Does he:

> Study pronunciation
> Correct the malformation of teeth
> Manipulate a patient's back to relieve pain
> Study evolution

47

General Knowledge

1 Which British soldier commanded the victorious force that captured Quebec in 1759?
Was it:

>Viscount Cunningham
>James Wolfe
>Sir Arthur Wellesley
>Sir James Outram

2 Who was the Mexican general who was appointed president of Mexico five times and lost two wars fought against the U.S.A.?
Was he:

>Antonio Santa Anna
>Benito Juarez
>Emiliano Zapata
>Battista Marquez

3 Which American general was relieved of his command during the Korean War in 1951?
Was it:

>Zachary Taylor
>Joseph Stilwell
>Douglas MacArthur
>William Calley

4 Who was the last British monarch to command an army on the battlefield?
Was it:

> Charles II
> William III
> George II
> Charles I

5 Who commanded the Chindits during the Second World War?
Was it:

> Chiang Kai-chek
> Orde Wingate
> Marshal Tito
> Edward Winslow

6 Who was the Commander-in-Chief of the Allied Forces in North Africa in 1942?
Was it:

> Dwight Eisenhower
> Viscount Montgomery
> Sir Harold Alexander
> Winston Churchill

7 Which British First World War commander defeated the Turkish armies in Palestine in 1918?
Was it:

> Sir Archibald Murray
> T. E. Lawrence
> Viscount Allenby
> Sir John French

8 What was the name of the Prussian commander who reinforced Wellington's troops at the Battle of Waterloo ensuring the defeat of Napoleon's army?
Was it:

> Michel Ney
> Alfred von Tirpitz

Otto von Bismarck
Gebhard von Blücher

9 Which English king commanded the victorious army at the battle of Agincourt in 1415?
Was it:
> Edward III
> Henry V
> Edward I
> Richard the Lionheart

10 Where was the British General John Burgoyne fighting when he was defeated at the battle of Saragossa in 1777?
Was he:
> In Spain
> In Portugal
> In America
> In Bavaria

48

World-wide

1 Which is the largest island in the world?
Is it:

> Great Britain
> Borneo
> Greenland
> Madagascar

2 Which is the longest river in the world?
Is it:

> The Amazon
> The Nile
> The Yangtze Kiang
> The Zaïre (Congo)

3 Which language is the most widely spoken on earth?
Is it:

> Spanish
> English
> Mandarin (Chinese)
> Hindi

4 On which of these lines of latitude can you sail all the way round the earth without touching land?
Is it:

> 45° north
> 45° south

30° south
60° south

5 Which is the largest lake in the world?
Is it:

       The Black Sea
       The Caspian Sea
       Lake Victoria
       Lake Superior

6 Which great Asian river flows into the sea near the port of Karachi?
Is it:

       The Indus
       The Salween
       The Ganges
       The Brahmaputra

7 To which country does Easter Island belong?
Is it:

       Australia
       Britain
       Chile
       The U.S.A.

8 Which is the largest state in Australia from the point of view of area?
Is it:

       Western Australia
       Queensland
       Northern Territory
       South Australia

9 What is the name of the small Himalayan kingdom which lies north of Bangladesh?
Is it:

       Nepal
       Bhutan
       Kashmir
       Tibet

10 Where is Patagonia?
Is it:

>In northern Spain
>In southern Argentina
>In Central America
>In the toe of Italy

49

Sound of Music

1 In which musical film does the song 'You Are My Lucky Star' feature?
Is it:

> *Seven Brides for Seven Brothers*
> *The Boy Friend*
> *Singin' in the Rain*
> *Annie Get Your Gun*

2 Who wrote the musical *There's No Business Like Show Business*?
Was it:

> George Gershwin
> Richard Rodgers
> Irving Berlin
> Oscar Hammerstein

3 Which French novelist wrote the original story that was later transformed into the musical *Gigi*?
Was it:

> Georges Sand
> Victor Hugo
> Colette
> Guy de Maupassant

4 Lucille Ball starred in a musical filmed in 1973, when she was sixty-three. What was its title?
Was it:

> *Mame*
> *Fiddler on the Roof*
> *Godspell*
> *Oklahoma!*

5 Who plays the part of the night club compère in the musical *Cabaret*?
Is it:

> Michael York
> Cliff Richard
> Joel Grey
> Joel Barnett

6 Which actress mimes to Marni Nixon's singing voice in the film version of *My Fair Lady*?
Is it:

> Leslie Caron
> Audrey Hepburn
> Natalie Wood
> Kim Novak

7 In which film does the highly successful song 'Raindrops Keep Falling On My Head' act as a theme tune?
Is it:

> *Singin' In The Rain*
> *The Thomas Crown Affair*
> *Butch Cassidy and the Sundance Kid*
> *The Man From La Mancha*

8 Which of Shakespeare's plays provides the plot for the musical *Kiss Me Kate*?
Is it:

> *The Comedy of Errors*
> *All's Well That End's Well*

The Taming of the Shrew
Love's Labours Lost

9 Who wrote the novel *Lost Horizon* which was later adapted into a musical of the same name?
Was it:

> Peter Finch
> Joseph Conrad
> James Hilton
> Ian Fleming

10 In which of Gilbert and Sullivan's operettas does the character Nankipoo appear?
Is it:

> *H.M.S. Pinafore*
> *Patience*
> *Iolanthe*
> *The Mikado*

50

Famous for What?

1 What is the town of Stilton famous for?
Is it:

        Hot springs
        Salt
        Cheese
        Beer

2 What famous wine growing area of France is centred around the city of Reims?
Is it:

        Burgundy
        Bordeaux
        Cognac
        Champagne

3 Why is Lord Lister famous?
Did he:

        Introduce the use of anaesthetics to medical science
        Discover the circulation of the blood
        Introduce the use of antiseptics into hospitals
        Perform the first kidney transplant

4 Whose wife is/was famous for her cooking and culinary skills?

Is it:

> Mr Cradock
> Mr Beeton
> Mr Carrier
> Mr Ronay

5 In which sport is the Marquis of Queensberry best remembered?
Is it:

> Horse racing
> Shooting
> Tennis
> Boxing

6 What is Stanley Gibbons famous for among collectors?
Is it:

> Wild animals
> Postage stamps
> Porcelain
> Coins

7 For what is Grace Darling famous?
Is it:

> Assisting Florence Nightingale
> Discovering the Darling River in Australia
> Her bravery in rescuing shipwrecked sailors
> Her famous performances as Shakespeare's heroines

8 What was *The Flying Scotsman*?
Was it:

> **A** very select brand of malt whisky
> **A** steam locomotive
> An inter-island ferry in the Hebrides
> The first London-Edinburgh scheduled passenger aircraft

9 For what product is the town of Sèvres famous?
Is it:

> Pâté de foie gras
> Velvet
> Porcelain
> Silk

10 Who was the famous spy in the First World War who acted as a double agent until shot by the French in 1917?
Was it:

> Pavlova
> Edith Cavell
> Eric Blair
> Mata Hari

Answers

1. ALL STARS

1 Henry II.

2 Robert Shaw.

3 Mary Tyler Moore.

4 'Play it, Sam'.

5 Seven children.

6 *On the Waterfront.*

7 All four of them. Alice White and Ruth Taylor starred in the 1928 version and Marilyn Monroe and Jane Russell in the 1953 version.

8 David Niven.

9 Joanna Shimkus.

10 Arthur Miller.

2. THE ANCIENT WORLD

1 Octavius Caesar.

2 Carthaginian.

3 Archimedes.

4 The Forum.

5 Aeneas.

6 Macedonia.

7 Poetry.

8 Julius Caesar.

9 Socrates.

10 A ship.

3. MEN AT THE TOP

1 William Pitt (the younger).

2 The first Secretary-General of the U.N.

3 Konrad Adenauer.

4 Chiang Kai-chek.

5 Lord Killanin.

6 Hugh Gaitskell.

7 Adrian IV.

8 Czechoslovakia.

9 Central African Empire.

10 J. B. Page.

4. BRAVE NEW WORLD

1 Dallas.
2 Russia.
3 Lord Cornwallis.
4 New Amsterdam.
5 A Texan garrison massacred by Mexicans.
6 Robert E. Lee.
7 In the Hawaiian Islands.
8 Amerigo Vespucci.
9 Edward H. White.
10 The pilot of a spy plane shot down in 1960.

5. COLOUR CONSCIOUS

1 Bright yellow.
2 In Calcutta.
3 Marlene Dietrich.
4 An R.A.F. display team.
5 A literary and studious woman.
6 Red Rum.
7 A British military force.
8 An excessively sentimental piece of writing.
9 In a theatre.
10 Francisco Franco.

6. ALL AT SEA

1 Between the North Sea and the Baltic.
2 In the Atlantic off the coast of South America.
3 Africa.
4 The *Titanic*.
5 Bartolomew Diaz.
6 The Bosporus, the sea of Marmara and the Dardanelles in that order.
7 Jacques-Yves Cousteau.
8 Seaweed.
9 The ships which evacuated troops from Dunkirk.
10 A mark on the hulls of merchant ships.

7. MYTHS AND LEGENDS

1 Thor.
2 Agamemnon.
3 The resting place of warriors killed in battle.
4 Sir Galahad.
5 Atlas.
6 Aphrodite.
7 Troubles and misery.
8 Icarus.
9 *Pygmalion.*
10 Orpheus.

8. WHO SAID?

1 Abraham Lincoln.
2 Jaques in *As You Like It.*
3 'Dr Livingstone, I presume'.
4 During the advance of the French infantry at **Waterloo**.
5 Mae West.
6 Queen Victoria.
7 Helen of Troy.
8 *Rowan and Martin's Laugh-in.*
9 The Battle of Egypt.
10 Niccolò Machiavelli.

9. HIGHSPOTS

1 K.2., or Chogori (K.2. is its more common name).
2 Alaska.
3 On Sicily.
4 The Urals.
5 The Zugspitze.
6 Chris Bonington.
7 Bolivia.
8 The World Trade Centre.
9 The pyramid of Cheops.
10 Elephants.

10. NUMBERS

1 Three.
2 Twenty.
3 The fifth.
4 Directory enquiries.
5 The Chancellor of the Exchequer.
6 Twelve.
7 A stormy area of the ocean.
8 The 49th parellel.
9 Six days.
10 A thousand years.

11. EUREKA!

1 John Logie Baird.
2 Leonardo da Vinci.
3 Dissolve and make the water taste salty.
4 Violet.
5 Sir Rowland Hill.
6 Calculus.
7 Boiling a kettle.
8 The hovercraft.
9 The Nobel Prize.
10 Sir Barnes Wallis.

12. OLYMPIC GAMES

1 Chamonix.
2 At Olympia.
3 Romanian.
4 Mark Spitz.
5 Athens.
6 Richard Fosbury.
7 *Tokyo Olympiad*.
8 Lake Placid.
9 Twenty-one.
10 Mexico City.

13. -OLOGIES AND -ISMS

1 Strong self-interest and self-admiration.
2 The study of organic tissues.
3 Find water and control its distribution.
4 Pablo Picasso.
5 A similarity.
6 Abstain from pleasure.
7 Richard Sheridan's *The Rivals*.
8 An oriental philosophy and religion.
9 James VI.
10 Four.

14. LANDMARKS

1 At Rio de Janeiro.
2 St John Lateran.
3 New York.
4 Agra.
5 Lizard Point.
6 In Venice.
7 Carnac.
8 At the extreme south of South America.
9 The leaning tower.
10 The Dead Sea.

15. MAN AND WIFE

1 Jane Seymour.
2 Mrs Ernest Simpson.
3 Joanne Woodward.
4 Louis XVI.
5 Robert Browning.
6 Bassanio.
7 Mary Callaghan.
8 Lauren Bacall.
9 George, Prince of Denmark.
10 Ali McGraw.

16. FRACTIONS

1 U.S.S.R.
2 An eighth.
3 Five-sevenths.
4 In india.
5 Micro-.
6 The Charge of the Light Brigade.
7 Four-fifths.
8 A furlong.
9 His wife.
10 A radius.

17. DEATH AND DISASTER

1 Aberfan.
2 Dag Hammerskjöld.
3 The Great Fire.
4 Both Jean-Paul Marat and Agamemnon.
5 In Westminster Abbey.
6 Bucharest.
7 Pompeii.
8 Jack Ruby.
9 White.
10 The Black Death.

18. WORLD CITIES

1 London.
2 Ecuador.
3 Damascus.
4 Memphis.
5 On the North Island of New Zealand.
6 Saigon.
7 Washington.
8 Pavia.
9 Edinburgh.
10 Nagasaki.

19. CRIME AND PUNISHMENT

1 'Acts of gross indecency'.
2 John Christie.
3 Poaching.
4 The Battle of Sedgemoor.
5 Blofeld.
6 In Madame Tussaud's.
7 A prison in San Francisco Bay.
8 In French Guiana.
9 Ned Kelly.
10 Fyodor Mikhailovich Dostoevsky.

20. INITIALS

1 Royal Aircraft Establishment.
2 The Parliamentary Labour Party.
3 Agricultural Research Council.
4 The Campaign Against Racial Discrimination.
5 Intermediate-range ballistic missile.
6 Organization of Central American States.
7 Indian Medical Service.
8 A Fellow of the Royal College of Organists.
9 Central Council for Physical Recreation.
10 The Department of Education and Science.

21. BOOK-WORM

1 Alex Haley.
2 Adolf Hitler.
3 James Herriot.
4 Peter Benchley.
5 In Chicago.
6 Thomas Hardy.
7 Polish.
8 James Boswell.
9 John Evelyn.
10 *The Love Girl and The Innocent*; the others are novels by Solzhenitsyn.

22. FIGURES OF SPEECH

1 The use of contradictory words in a single statement.

2 A general understatement.

3 The use of exaggeration for terms of emphasis.

4 The assumption that natural things have feelings like human beings.

5 The use of words that repeat the same consonant.

6 A hint or a suggestion.

7 The use of words which reproduce or echo the sounds they suggest.

8 A sharp, memorable quip or saying.

9 The descent from lofty to trivial things.

10 Unnecessary repetition.

23. CHEERS!

1 Very Special Old Pale.

2 The blind monk who first invented champagne.

3 Alexander.

4 The town of Jerez in Spain.

5 The Duke of Clarence, brother of Richard III.

6 Blackcurrants.

7 A mixture of Guinness and champagne.

8 Quinine.

9 All of them do this.

10 Rye and barley are both used.

24. WORLD ALLIANCES

1 Switzerland.

2 The Communist counterpart of the European Community.

3 Pakistan.

4 Greece.

5 Austrian.

6 Seven.

7 The European Economic Community.

8 Australasia.

9 Both Japan and Italy.

10 Turkey.

25. STREETS AHEAD

1 A river.
2 *Quality Street.*
3 In Dublin.
4 Tennessee Williams.
5 Ermine Street.
6 Hack writers.
7 Ralph McTell.
8 Garrick Street.
9 Vincent Van Gogh.
10 To remove prostitution from the streets.

26. FUNNY HA HA

1 The Keystone Cops.
2 Both Stan Laurel and Oliver Hardy.
3 Stanley Holloway.
4 Zeppo.
5 *Passport to Pimlico.*
6 George Burns.
7 A priceless gem.
8 *Carry on Sergeant.*
9 Hattie Jacques.
10 Ronald Searle.

27. RESIDENT ALIENS

1 According to the menu.
2 Make a tactless comment.
3 The Prince of Wales.
4 A drunken man speaks the truth.
5 A striking theatrical effect.
6 Essays or poems.
7 A special object of dislike.
8 Make good use of the present.
9 Having difficulty in choosing with so much to choose from.
10 The Royal Air Force.

28. NATURE TRAIL

1 The giant squid.
2 The cheetah.
3 The blue whale.
4 Carry their young in pouches.
5 The domestic dog.
6 A young salmon.
7 Guy.
8 The albatross.
9 On its back.
10 The ostrich.

29. NUMBER ONE

1 Alcock and Brown.
2 *A Hard Day's Night*.
3 St Augustine.
4 White ermine.
5 Viv Anderson.
6 A partridge.
7 'Thou shalt have no other gods before me'.
8 Tottenham Hotspur.
9 *The Jazz Singer*.
10 Caen.

30. ON FOUR WHEELS

1 Universal joints.
2 Grand Touring.
3 A carburettor and sparking plugs.
4 At present it alternates between Brands Hatch and Silverstone.
5 Jack Brabham.
6 The Volkswagen Beetle.
7 Lord Nuffield.
8 'Blue Flame'.
9 Juan-Manuel Fangio.
10 American.

31. COMPOSERS

1 One.
2 Franz Lehár.
3 Igor Stravinsky.
4 Franz Joseph Haydn.
5 Leonard Bernstein.
6 The Battle of Borodino.
7 Pierre de Beaumarchias.
8 Sir Edward Elgar.
9 Felix Mendelssohn.
10 Johann Sebastian Bach.

32. SOLID FOUNDATIONS

1 The Prime Minister, it is his country residence.
2 To Arizona.
3 Notre Dame.
4 The Reichstag.
5 In Spain.
6 Zimbabwe.
7 Sir John Vanbrugh.
8 Knossos.
9 A statue.
10 The Capitol.

33. WHAM, ZAP, POW!

1 Marlon Brando.
2 Four.
3 *Fritz the Cat.*
4 *Snow White and the Seven Dwarfs.*
5 Max Fleischer.
6 Krypton.
7 Algy.
8 Lady Penelope.
9 *Skeleton Dance.*
10 Rudyard Kipling.

34. ALL TOGETHER NOW

1 George Fox.
2 One of the Inns of Court which admit law students.
3 A society for members of the Conservative Party.
4 Lord Baden-Powell.
5 The Musketeers.
6 The Sunnites.
7 The Chartists.
8 The Argonauts.
9 Horses.
10 Love and care for mankind.

35. ENERGY

1 U.S.S.R.
2 Both 746 watts and the power required to raise 550 lbs one foot in one second.
3 Joule.
4 U.S.A.
5 In 1975.
6 Electricity.
7 270–300 million years old.
8 10.6 km/l.
9 U.S.A.
10 Methane gas.

36. PLAYS AND PLAYERS

1 Christopher Marlowe.
2 Thomas More.
3 Che Guevara.
4 *The Beggar's Opera*.
5 John Osborne.
6 Rupert Davies.
7 Richard Burton.
8 *Ross*.
9 Maggie Smith.
10 *The Tempest*.

37. WORLD AT WAR

1 Meerut.
2 Nine.
3 The Thirty Years' War.
4 The Zulu War.
5 *Guernica.*
6 Zanzibar.
7 115 years.
8 In 1839–1842.
9 The War of Jenkins' Ear.
10 *The Gallic Wars.*

38. MEASURE FOR MEASURE

1 To measure quantities of heat.
2 6 feet.
3 1000.
4 112.
5 Beverages.
6 Earthquakes.
7 6080 ft.
8 A barrel.
9 A whole gale.
10 $2\frac{1}{2}$ lbs.

39. UNDERGROUND

1 Le Métro.
2 Moorgate.
3 New York.
4 In London.
5 London.
6 Upminster.
7 At Shepherd's Bush.
8 The City and South London Railway.
9 There is no underground railway in the city centre.
10 The Jubilee Line.

40. FLOCCINAUCINIHILIPILIFICATION

1 Occupying a day.
2 Comprising both water and land.
3 An ornamental screen at the back of an altar.
4 A series of variations for the bagpipe.
5 The period between one king and his successor.
6 Calculate it by using a series of other terms.
7 The combination of two adjacent vowels.
8 Mornful and gloomy.
9 Someone who is preoccupied with their state of health.
10 A dunghill.

41. SAILOR BEWARE

1 Joshua Slocum.
2 *Robertson's Golly.*
3 Discover America.
4 *The Pelican* was renamed *The Golden Hind* after she rounded Cape Horn. So both are correct.
5 Vasco da Gama.
6 Horatio Hornblower.
7 Maarten Tromp.
8 The *Tirpitz.*
9 At Calvi.
10 The *Niña.*

42. THE BIBLE

1 Leviticus.
2 Psalm 119.
3 Moses.
4 Salome.
5 Revelation.
6 Joseph.
7 Wisdom.
8 Manoah.
9 Lazarus.
10 The criminal who was released by Pontius Pilate in place of Jesus Christ.

43. FOR GALLANTRY

1 The George Cross.
2 Paul Revere.
3 John Cornwell.
4 Leonidas.
5 German airmen.
6 Sir Henry Havelock.
7 The inhabitants of Malta.
8 Horatius.
9 One that is awarded after the death of the person to whom it is presented.
10 For saving life at sea or on land.

44. WHAT'S IN A NAME?

1 Samuel Clemens.
2 Lenin.
3 Dutch Guiana.
4 Ehrich Weiss.
5 Hector Hugh Munro.
6 Viscount Hailsham.
7 Lesley Hornby.
8 A sore throat and a heavy cold.
9 *Pride and Prejudice.*
10 Charles Lutwidge Dodgson.

45. SPACE TRAVEL

1 Vostok I.
2 Apollo VIII.
3 Richard Nixon.
4 Mars.
5 Czech.
6 In Houston.
7 *Blue Streak.*
8 Werner von Braun.
9 *Salyut.*
10 Michael Collins.

46. JOB LOT

1 Deal in insurance.
2 Study and explore caves.
3 Compile dictionaries.
4 Act as an usher to the Lord Chamberlain's department.
5 A beachcomber.
6 Supervise the stocking and issue of provisions on board ship.
7 Write in shorthand.
8 Maps.
9 To make gold out of base metals.
10 Correct the malformation of teeth.

47. GENERAL KNOWLEDGE

1 James Wolfe.
2 Antonio Santa Anna.
3 Douglas MacArthur.
4 George II.
5 Orde Wingate.
6 Dwight Eisenhower.
7 Viscount Allenby.
8 Gebhard von Blücher
9 Henry V
10 In America.

48. WORLD-WIDE

1 Greenland.
2 The Nile.
3 Mandarin (Chinese).
4 60° south.
5 The Caspian Sea.
6 The Indus.
7 Chile.
8 Western Australia.
9 Bhutan.
10 In Southern Argentina.

49. SOUND OF MUSIC

1 Both *The Boyfriend* and *Singin' in the Rain*.
2 Irving Berlin.
3 Colette.
4 *Mame*.
5 Joel Grey.
6 Audrey Hepburn.
7 *Butch Cassidy and the Sundance Kid*.
8 *The Taming of the Shrew*.
9 James Hilton.
10 *The Mikado*.

50. FAMOUS FOR WHAT?

1 Cheese.
2 Champagne.
3 Introduce the use of antiseptics into hospitals.
4 Mr Cradock and Mr Beeton.
5 Boxing.
6 Postage stamps.
7 Her bravery in rescuing shipwrecked sailors.
8 A steam locomotive.
9 Porcelain.
10 Mata Hari.

PART TWO

1000 MINDBOGGLERS

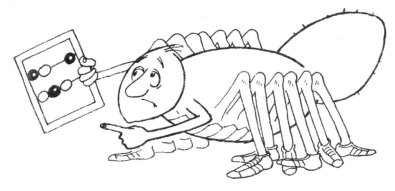

1. How many legs does a spider have?

2. What is 'geology'?

3. What was the Christian name of Queen Victoria's consort?

4. What nationality was the ancient general called Hannibal?

5. Which Italian city is famous for its leaning tower?

6. What do the initials B.V.M. stand for?

7. Which is the second largest country on earth?

8. Who was the English general who defeated Napoleon at the battle of Waterloo in 1815?

9. Which is the largest mammal living on earth?

10. Who is supposed to have placed his cloak over a puddle so that Queen Elizabeth I could walk on it without wetting her feet?

11. William Shakespeare wrote one whole scene entirely in French in one of his history plays. Which play is it?

12. Who was the famous band-leader who disappeared in an aircraft crash near the end of the Second World War?

13. Which architect designed St. Paul's Cathedral in London?

14. Which is the largest island on earth?

15. A dozen is 12. How much is a gross?

16. Who was the famous Venetian merchant who travelled to China and worked at the court of Kublai Khan for several years?

17. What is the name of the river that flows through the capital of France?

18. How many violin concertos did William Tell write?

19. Who is supposed to have said, 'We are not amused'?

20. Where are the Atlas Mountains?

21. Which famous comedy team starred in the film 'Duck Soup'?

22. Who was the prophet whose teachings inspired the religion called Islam?

23. What do the initials N.A.S.A. stand for?

24. In what year did Pakistan and India become independent countries?

25. How many players are there in a cricket team?

26. Who wrote the famous choral work '*The Messiah*'?

27. Where was St. Thomas Becket murdered?

28. Who was the second man to step onto the surface of the moon?

29. What is the Russian alphabet called?

30. Which film starring Ingrid Bergman and Humphrey Bogart is named after a place in Africa?

31. By what name is the writer Samuel Clemens better known?

32. Where is Tierra del Fuego?

33. What and where is Saskatchewan?

34. What do the initials C.I.D. stand for?

35. Which is the capital city of Colombia?

36. Which king of England is supposed to have burnt the cakes?

37. In which city is the '*Sound of Music*' set?

38. What do silk worms feed on?

39. Where would you find a Plimsoll line?

40. During the seventeenth century he kept what has become the world's most famous diary. He also helped to establish the English Royal Navy. What was his name?

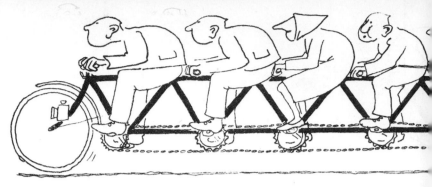

41. How many people ride a tandem?

42. What was the name of the wall built by the Romans north of Hadrian's wall?

43. Carnivorous means feeding on meat. What does omnivorous mean?

44. Which is larger: a litre or a quart?

45. How many kings called Edward have been crowned King of England?

46. Who was the first man to fly solo across the Atlantic?

47. What was the tallest construction in the ancient world?

48. Which group starred in the film 'Magical Mystery Tour'?

49. What nationality were the principal Impressionist painters?

50. Who climbed to the top of Mount Everest with Sir Edmund Hilary in 1953?

51. Which is the longest bone in the human body?

52. In Greek mythology who flew too near the sun and fell into the sea as a result?

53. What is the unit of currency used in the Soviet Union?

54. What mineral do ferrous metals contain?

55. In which book do you find the Apocrypha?

56. Who carved the famous statue of David in Florence?

57. What is the collective name for a group of lions?

58. What is the French name for the day we call Shrove Tuesday?

59. Which English playwright wrote '*The Importance of Being Earnest*'?

60. Where do the Basques live?

61. Which is the longest river in the western hemisphere?

62. What is a kipper?

63. Where are the Sea of Serenity and Ocean of Storms?

64. Of which country was Tutankhamen once King?

65. Who wrote the novel about the French Revolution called '*A Tale of Two Cities*'?

66. What nationality was Cleopatra?

67. What does an osteopath do?

68. Where in London would you go to see Nelson's Column?

69. What is Superman's other name?

70. Which city had the first underground railway?

71. What was Queen Elizabeth II's father called?

72. Who was the first man in space?

73. What is the colour of mourning in Moslem countries?

74. What was the former name of Kampuchea?

75. What was a Zeppelin?

76. What is the name given to the Russian equivalent of the American Skylab?

77. Where is the world's highest waterfall?

78. What is a vixen?

79. How many litres are there in one kilolitre?

80. Who invented the telephone?

81. Where is the House of Keys?

82. What nationality was the great painter Picasso?

83. What was the name of the ship in
which Sir Francis Drake sailed
round the world?

84. Two very famous Chinese political
leaders died in 1976. Name one of
them.

85. What is the name of the musical
based on George Bernard Shaw's
play 'Pygmalion'?

86. What is the capital city of Zimbabwe-
Rhodesia?

87. What is a more common word for
wedlock?

88. Why is Dame Margot Fonteyn
famous?

89. Which is the largest planet in the
solar system?

90. In which section of an orchestra would you find the *cor anglais?*

91. In which European country is the Black Forest?

92. Marie Antoinette was the wife of which King of France?

93. Bjorn Borg was the second man to win the Men's Singles at Wimbledon three years in succession. Who was the first to do this?

94. In which Italian city is the Fiat motor company based?

95. He worked for the Commonwealth government of Oliver Cromwell, he wrote an epic poem in English and he was blind when he died. Who was he?

96. What do the initials l.b.w. stand for in cricket?

97. Where are the smallest bones in the human body?

98. Who was President of the United States after John F. Kennedy?

99. Which is the principal language spoken in Brazil?

100. What is a wallaby?

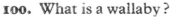

101. What is the ancient name for the Dardanelles?

102. Which is heavier a tonne of feathers or a tonne of coal?

103. How many people make up a sextet?

104. What was the name of the raft on which Thor Heyerdail's expedition crossed the Pacific in 1950?

105. What does a chiropodist do?

106. Which prophet led the Children of Israel out of Egypt to the Promised Land?

107. The Greeks called her Aphrodite. What did the Romans call her?

108. Why was Andrew Jackson famous?

109. What is the mineral used in the manufacture of aluminium?

110. In which large American city will you find Hollywood?

111. Why is William Wordsworth famous?

112. Which is the largest state in the USA?

113. Which is the only animal to sleep on its back?

114. Who signed Magna Carta in 1215?

115. What is the capital of El Salvador?

116. There are millions of SLR cameras throughout the world. What do the initials stand for?

117. What was the name of King Arthur's capital?

118. What is the name of the girlfriend of Popeye the Sailor?

119. In which religion are cows considered to be sacred?

120. What is the name of the rabbit in the film 'Bambi'?

121. Its Italian name is Monte Bianco.
What do the French call it?

122. Which is the only animal with 4
knees?

123. What is the Beaufort Scale used to
measure?

124. Which of the planets lies nearest the
sun?

125. In Britain what was the first postage
stamp used to be stuck on to
envelopes?

126. What is a sextant used for?

127. Who made the first flights in a
powered aircraft?

128. Henry VIII had six wives. Who was his first?

129. Who wrote the opera called 'The Flying Dutchman'?

130. What is the name of the volcano on the island of Sicily?

131. What is the largest meat-eating animal living in Britain?

132. Where do the Lapps live?

133. What two elements make up water?

134. On what side of the road do they drive in India?

135. What is the principal nerve in the human body?

136. Which Shakespearean character says, 'To be, or not to be: that is the question'?

137. MCMLXXX is the Roman number for what?

138. For what type of food is the town of Roquefort in France famous.

139. Which bird has the widest wing span?

140. What is semaphore?

141. In which film does the song 'Raindrops Keep Falling On My Head' feature?

142. What are Argentinian cowboys called?

143. Who found Dr. David Livingstone in Africa?

144. What was the name of the first balloon that successfully crossed the Atlantic in 1978?

145. What do the initials U.F.O. stand for?

146. What does a chrysalis become?

147. On what special occasion would you expect to use confetti?

148. What is roulette?

149. Which Roman general conquered Gaul?

150. Who painted The Mona Lisa?

151. What is the C.I.A. in the USA?

152. Which British admiral was killed in 1805?

153. When Tim Severin and his crew set sail for America in a leather boat from Ireland, whose voyage were they trying to re-enact?

154. Who was traditionally the patron saint of travellers?

155. What is scrumpy?

156. What element is used in creating atomic energy?

157. What is the name of Judy Garland's eldest daughter?

158. Moslems are forbidden by their religion to eat the meat of which animal?

159. What system of transport is Venice famous for?

160. Who wrote the musical 'South Pacific'?

161. What was the dodo?

162. What is the oldest national flag in the world?

163. Where does the British Prime Minister live?

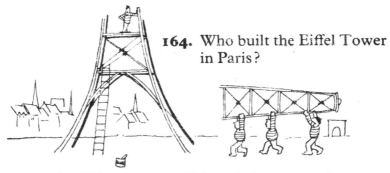

164. Who built the Eiffel Tower in Paris?

165. What is −40 Fahrenheit expressed in Centigrade?

166. What was the name of Romulus' brother?

167. What is an octahedron?

168. What is the name of Batman's young friend and helper?

169. Where is the Taj Mahal?

170. What was the name of the liner that hit an iceberg in the north Atlantic and sank in 1912?

171. What was the former name of Ho Chi-minh city?

172. The *Mayonnaise* is the national anthem of which country?

173. What does the Latin expression 'nota bene' (n.b.) mean?

174. In a Court of Law, who stands in the dock?

175. Which African country was invaded by Tanzania in 1979, leading to the overthrow of its head of state?

176. What is O.P.E.C.?

177. What is another word for timpani?

178. Who invented Sherlock Holmes?

179. On what scale are earthquakes measured?

180. In which Country are the 1986 Olympic Games to be held?

181. Lenin was once the leader of which great country?

182. What is the flag of the Royal Navy?

183. Who founded the Boy Scouts?

184. Where is Fifth Avenue?

185. Who invented dynamite?

186. Which British painter painted the Blue Boy?

187. What is the international distress signal?

188. Why is November called November?

189. According to popular belief what is the moon made of?

190. What should you call a group of geese?

191. Which British sportsman won the Men's Olympic Figure Skating championship in 1976?

192. The Victoria Cross is the highest decoration awarded in Britain. What is the next one after that?

193. Which famous tapestry was made to celebrate the Norman conquest of England in 1066?

194. There are two principal braking systems used in cars. One uses disc brakes, what does the other one use?

195. What was the code name given to the Allied invasion of Europe in 1944?

196. Which British universities provide teams for the annual University Boat Race?

197. Which aircraft is known as the 'Jumbo Jet'?

198. What is the name of the ferryman in Greek mythology who carries the souls of the dead across the River Styx to Hades?

199. What was the name of Nelson's flagship?

200. Which Himalayan kingdom lies north of Bangladesh?

201. Who are the native inhabitants of Australia?

202. Why is Indira Gandhi famous?

203. Where are the headquarters of the International Red Cross?

204. What is the capital of Canada?

205. Who or what is the yeti?

206. Who was killed in Khartoum in 1885?

207. Who was the United States President at the start of the Second World War?

208. Which is the longest river in Britain?

209. What is a geyser?

210. What do four quadrants make?

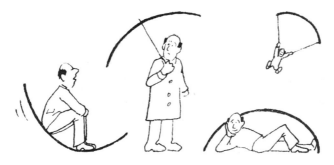

211. Whose motto is the German expression 'Ich Dien' ('I serve')?

212. What do oak trees grow from?

213. Who became President of France after General Charles De Gaulle?

214. Which British theatrical company is based at Stratford-upon-Avon?

215. What is Dutch Guiana now called?

216. What are the 'dramatis personae'?

217. Who composed 'The Planets'?

218. Who was the first man to walk in space?

219. What material is made out of jute?

220. What are marsupials?

221. Which famous silent screen comedian died on Christmas Day 1977?

222. Which racing driver became World Champion in 1976?

223. What is the fastest production car in the world?

224. What was the old name for Istanbul?

225. What well known spirit is drunk in Russia?

226. What is another name for Santa Claus?

227. Washington D.C. is the capital of the United States of America. What does D.C. stand for?

228. Who was the first television Simon Templar in 'The Saint'?

229. Why is Leif Ericsson famous?

230. Who wrote the 'Famous Five' stories?

231. What was the name given to female campaigners for the right to vote for women?

232. Who was the priest who was one of Robin Hood's band?

233. Which river forms the border between France and Germany, flows from Switzerland to the North Sea and is famous for the wine on its banks?

234. What is a condor?

235. Which is the largest ocean on earth?

236. What is polo?

237. Of which great empire was Nero once emperor?

238. Which happened first, the Great Fire of London or the Plague?

239. Who was the British Prime Minister at the start of the Second World War?

240. What is the name of the vertical take-off aircraft developed by Hawker-Siddeley?

241. What is the name for a young swan?

242. What is the capital city of Pakistan?

243. Which planet is surrounded by
rings that make it unique?

244. In the nursery rhyme, what jumped
over the moon?

245. Which is longer a nautical mile or a
land mile?

246. How many disciples were appointed
by Jesus Christ?

247. Where was porcelain first made?

248. What is Tarzan's girlfriend called?

249. What type of music do you associate
with the Caribbean?

250. What was the name of the first steam engine to run on the Stockton & Darlington railway?

251. What does Laurence Olivier do for a living?

252. Into which country in Europe is Serbia now incorporated?

253. In which country would you find the Sugar Loaf Mountain?

254. What is the square of twelve?

255. Who wrote the James Bond novels?

256. What is convectional rainfall?

257. What is the name of the object that is hit and flicked across the ice in ice-hockey?

258. Diesel engines lack one noticeable feature present in petrol engines. What is it?

259. What was the name of the large units into which the Roman army was divided?

260. Who did the actress Grace Kelly marry?

261. Who wrote the novel 'Treasure Island'?

262. What is the deepest depression on earth?

263. What does the French word *montague* mean?

264. Where is Wall Street?

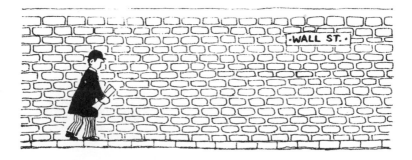

265. What is another name for a lexicon?

266. Who said, 'A horse, a horse, my kingdom for a horse'?

267. What was Walt Disney's first cartoon character called?

268. What do the initials G.M.T. stand for?

269. What are the highest clouds called?

270. What does the prefix kilo- mean?

271. Where is the Golden Gate Bridge?

272. When is Maundy Thursday?

273. What is fives?

274. Where was a famous 'tea-party' held in 1773?

275. To which fish family does the tuna belong?

276. What is the name of the second book in the Old Testament?

277. What was the name of the Italian dictator during the Second World War?

278. What is a dromedary?

279. For what is Thomas Chippendale famous?

280. What vegetable eaten in summer is named after an island in the Aegean?

281. What is another name for the illness tetanus?

282. What was a guinea?

283. Which island in the Hebrides is famous for its tweed?

284. What is celebrated in France every year on 14th July?

285. What is the next number in the sequence 2, 5, 11, 23 ... ?

286. According to tradition what animals desert a sinking ship?

287. Where is the Pentagon?

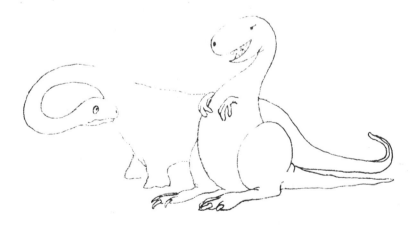

288. What was 'Tyrannosaurus rex'?

289. What is the name of the character invented by Daniel Defoe who lived on a desert island?

290. What is the common name for sodium chloride?

291. There were fourteen kings called Ptolemy. Which country did they rule?

292. Which animal is normally measured in 'hands'?

293. Who was the first Tzar of Russia?

294. What is Calcutta famous for in British history?

295. Which king was visited by the Queen of Sheba?

296. In which sport has Sir Donald Bradman become a legend?

297. What is the unit of currency used in Spain?

298. Which fresh water fish is also called a jack?

299. Which ancient city was engulfed by the lava from the volcano Vesuvius?

300. Who invented the Wellington bomber and the bouncing bomb?

301. What are the sirocco and the mistral?

302. Which landmark in London is famous for its ravens?

217

303. When is Armistice Day?

304. Who was the Roman god of war?

305. What was the name given to an early bicycle with a very big front wheel and a very small back wheel?

306. If someone is 'droll' what are they?

307. How was William Cody better known?

308. Where would you expect to find a duck-billed platypus?

309. What is the popular name given to leading bankers and financiers in the Swiss city of Zurich?

310. For what is Isambard Brunel best remembered?

311. What is measured in reams?

312. What happens to you if you are suffering from amnesia?

313. Who first flew across the English Channel in an aeroplane?

314. What is regicide?

315. Apart from gold and myrrh, what other gift did the three kings bring to the infant Jesus?

316. What event in the Olympic Games is named after an ancient battle?

317. What was the name of the flag flown by pirates?

318. Where in your body would you expect to develop a cataract?

319. With what do you associate the name of Mrs. Beeton?

320. From which country do the Springbok rugby teams come?

321. How many steps are there in John Buchan's famous novel?

322. What was the Christian name of the Black Prince?

323. What is measured by a Geiger counter?

324. From which fish is caviar obtained?

325. Which American President was shot while he was watching a play?

326. Which woollen head garment is named after a battle in the Crimean War?

327. What were discovered in the Lascaux caves in 1940?

328. Which soldier said, 'Veni, vidi, vici'?

329. Which is the second highest mountain in the world?

330. In which ancient civilisation were cats worshipped?

331. To whom was Guinevere married?

332. Where were the famous Hanging Gardens?

333. Where do avalanches happen?

334. From which city did the Orient Express leave on its journey to Istanbul?

335. Who composed the 'Pastoral' symphony?

336. How many lines are there in a sonnet?

337. Who is the Church of England's 'top priest'?

338. What is the name of Agatha Christie's famous Belgian detective?

339. What is the group name for a collection of ants?

340. What happened in Glencoe?

341. Which is the largest church in the world?

342. How many events are there in the pentathalon?

343. What nationality was the first man to reach the South Pole?

344. James Boswell wrote his biography. Who was he?

345. For what was Samson famous?

346. The United States bought a country from Russia for 2 cents an acre. Which country?

347. By what name was Aircraftsman Shaw better known?

348. What is the name for a Tibetan priest?

349. Where do you play curling?

350. Which Pakistani politician was hanged in 1979?

351. What is the square of 11?

352. What do you measure with a calorimeter?

353. Where do Moslems worship?

354. Who made the famous statement, 'The end justifies the means'?

355. Where are deltas formed?

356. What animal apart from man, has a life expectancy of 70 years?

357. Which English king brought about the dissolution of the monasteries in the 1530's?

358. What is the outer covering of haggis?

359. What are the Great Bear and the Little Bear?

360. What is an abacus used for?

361. Who wrote operettas with W.S. Gilbert?

362. Which chemical helps our bones grow strong?

363. Who is supposed to have played the fiddle while Rome was burning?

364. What do the initials COD mean?

365. Where in the world is the veldt?

366. Who was first knighted by Queen Elizabeth II for sailing solo around the world?

367. What is the symbol for the sign of the zodiac called Aries?

368. Where is the Wailing Wall?

369. What does a cartographer do?

370. What was the author of '*The Lord of the Rings*' by profession?

371. Where was El Greco born?

372. Which game begins with a 'bully off'?

373. Jesus was born in Bethlehem. Where was he brought up?

374. What is Stonehenge?

375. What are the initials of the French national railway company?

376. From which fruit is the liqueur Kirsch made?

377. What is a marlinspike used for?

378. What is the collective noun for trout?

379. The world's longest insect can grow up to 45 cm in length. What is it called?

380. What winter sport takes place on the Cresta run?

381. What was the name of the Viking who discovered Greenland in 982?

382. Where in the ancient world was the statue called the Colossus?

383. What is the name of the rabbit in the stories by A.A.Milne?

384. What would you be if you were called greenfingered?

385. What does a chronometer do?

386. What do you use if you play Russian roulette?

387. In Jereme K. Jerome's novel how many men are there in a boat?

388. What did Robert von Bunsen invent in 1855?

389. How many people play the game solitaire?

390. What is the name for the lines on maps that indicate elevation?

391. What is the next number in the sequence 36, 48, 60, 72 ... ?

392. Where would you expect to see a mirage?

393. Where did the boomerang originate?

394. Where is Arthur's Seat?

395. What is the title of George Orwell's novel about life in the future?

396. What type of craftsman would you be if you used an adze?

397. On what tree does spaghetti grow?

398. From which fruit is marmalade made?

399. Which metal is a liquid in normal conditions?

400. Which is the Holy city in Saudi Arabia to which Moslems make their pilgrimages?

401. Which side of a ship is the port side?

402. What is Lloyd's famous for?

403. What is the name of the largest island off the east coast of Africa?

404. Who pioneered modern nursing through her work in the Crimean War?

405. In Roman Numerals what does the letter C stand for?

406. What special royal event took place in 1977?

407. What nationality is Pope John-Paul II?

408. Who was 'the boy who never grew up'?

409. What is the common English name for a Tuxedo?

410. What is the national bird of New Zealand?

411. Koala bears feed on the leaves of what type of trees?

412. Why is Valentina Tereshkova famous?

413. What do the initials F.B.I. stand for?

414. What is *pâté de fois gras* made from?

415. What colour is the blood in the arteries?

416. What was the old name for Sri Lanka?

417. Who was Odin?

418. In connection with which sport was Joe Louis famous?

419. Who first flew across the Atlantic non-stop?

420. Mandarin Chinese and English are the world's two most widely spoken languages. What is the third?

421. What was the name of the largest diamond ever found?

422. Where did the assassination which started the First World War take place?

423. What was the name of the German general who was called the 'Desert Fox'?

424. Where in a car would you find the clutch?

425. Which fictional bear is named after a London railway terminus?

426. What is the name of the government on the Isle of Man?

427. What was the Christian name of Henry VIII's son?

428. Cardinal Richelieu was a statesman in which European country?

429. What poisonous gas is contained in the exhaust fumes from cars?

430. What is the name of the organs through which fish breathe?

431. In the game of croquet what do you use to strike the ball?

432. Alexander Dubček was leader of which Communist country until 1968?

433. What is the oldest city in the world?

434. How long did Jesus Christ spend in the wilderness?

435. Which city in the world has the largest population?

436. What was the name of the Frenchman who wrote *Around the World in Eighty Days*?

437. The mark is the unit of currency in which European country?

438. What is the name of the French oceanographer who made important developments in under-water swimming apparatus?

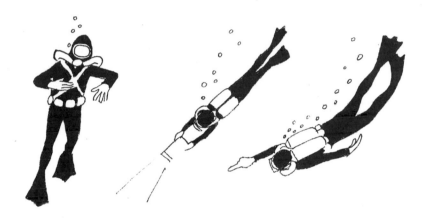

439. The areas, like counties, into which Switzerland is sub-divided have a special name. What is it?

440. Who is the patron saint of Scotland?

441. What valuable material is obtained from elephants?

442. Which American city is situated close to the San Andreas Fault?

443. Which English king commanded the sea to retreat and got his feet wet as a result?

444. Which is the longest Psalm?

445. Can you name Emily Bronte's two sisters?

446. In which American state is the old London Bridge now standing?

447. Which game do you play with a shuttlecock?

448. Who shot Lee Harvey Oswald?

449. Which saint is associated with wild animals?

450. Sanskrit used to be the language of which eastern country?

451. Which young animal is called a leveret?

452. In which European country is the Blarney Stone?

453. In North America it is called a diaper. What is it called in Britain?

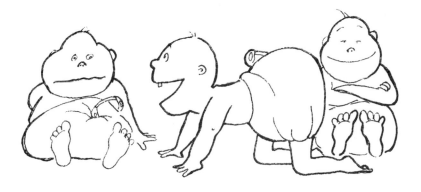

454. What drink do you associate with Brazil?

455. Who wrote the song *I Want to Hold Your Hand?*

456. What are incisors?

457. What two metals combine to make bronze?

458. What is the instrument used to measure altitude?

459. Who sits on the Woolsack?

460. Where would you expect to find a portcullis?

461. What is an artichoke?

462. Which American playwright wrote 'The Crucible'?

463. Which other country joined the European Economic Community on 1 January 1975 with Britain and Ireland?

464. Which is the strongest bone in the body?

465. What does VAT mean?

466. Who was the American Secretary of State who negotiated the end of the Vietnam War and was awarded the Nobel Peace Prize?

467. What does the Italian expression '*al fresco*' mean?

468. What is the rumba?

469. What colour is an emerald?

470. Who first sang '*Rock around the Clock*'?

471. Which Italian republic used to be governed by the doge?

472. What is the name of Don Quixote's companion?

473. Which capital city is sometimes called the Venice of the North?

474. What was the name of the liner that was sunk by German submarine off the coast of Ireland in 1915?

475. Which is the tallest animal in the world?

476. In which country is the Markka the unit of currency?

477. Who invented the gramophone?

478. What happens to you if you take a narcotic?

479. What are quavers, semi-quavers, breves and semi-breves?

480. If you saw a car with the letters CH on the back, which country would that car have come from?

481. What is the name of the reading system used by the blind?

482. Into which sea does the River Danube flow?

483. Where on a fish's body is the dorsal fin?

484. What do the initials BBC stand for?

485. What is the opposite of the port side?

486. Into how many degrees is a circle divided?

487. Which car was given the name the 'Tin Lizzie'?

488. Which British bomber of the Second World War was mostly built out of plywood?

489. What was the name later given to Cape Canaveral?

490. How many years have couples been married when they celebrate their golden wedding anniversaries?

491. What nationality is the motor racing driver Niki Lauda?

492. What important drug was discovered during the Second World War by Sir Alexander Fleming?

493. What is the common name for calcium carbonate?

494. What is the largest denomination bank note issued in England?

495. Thomas Sheraton was a great craftsman. What was he famous for making?

496. When is St. David's day?

497. Who wrote the popular musical 'Jesus Christ Superstar'?

498. With which art form is the name of Henri Matisse associated?

499. What does André Previn do for a living?

500. How would you represent the number 1509 in Roman numerals?

501. What was a mastodon?

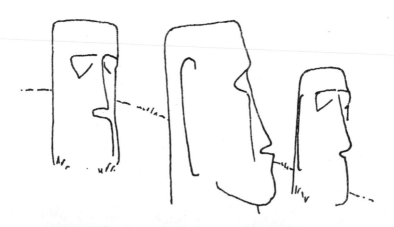

502. Which Pacific island is the home of many carved faces and statues of its earlier inhabitants?

503. Which mineral is used to make the leads in pencil?

504. What did Chopin, Mozart, Delius and Mahler have in common?

505. Which form of transport do you associate with the name Harley Davidson?

506. Monks live in monasteries, where do nuns live?

507. What would you find in the Sargasso Sea?

508. Who first started to build the Tower of London?

509. What decoration is the DSC?

510. William Shakespeare wrote a play about a Scottish king. What was the play called?

511. Who were the first people to use fingerprints as a form of legal identification?

512. What type of drink is produced in the region of Cognac in south-west France?

513. Over three-quarters of normal dry air is made up of one gas. Which gas is it?

514. What branch in medicine is covered by Geriatrics?

515. Who is the only boxer to have won the World Heavyweight Championship three times?

516. Which team from the Netherlands won the European Cup in 1971, −72, −73?

517. From which port in north-west Wales do the ferries run to Ireland?

518. What is the registration initial for motor vehicles registered in West Germany?

519. Who was the magician at the court of King Arthur?

520. Where was the German fleet scuttled after the First World War?

521. What is a double sheet bend?

522. There are four oceans in the world. Which is the largest?

523. Which of the tropics lies north of the Equator, the Tropic of Capricorn or the Tropic of Cancer?

524. What trees do you commonly find in graveyards?

525. Which famous French cartoon character was created by Hergé?

526. Which season is called the Fall in the USA?

527. Which volcano erupted in 1883, causing the most violent explosion in recent times?

528. Which airport in Ireland has the same name as an Irish river?

529. What type of animal is the 'black widow'?

530. Where in the world are the Netherlands Antilles?

531. What unit of measurement represents the distance travelled by light in one year?

532. There is only one member of the Most Illustrious Order of St. Patrick. Who do you think it is?

533. Which was the first single released by the Beatles, in 1962?

534. What do the letters r.p.m. represent?

535. With what type of musical instruments would you connect the name Stradivarius?

536. In which capital city were the first modern Olympic Games held in 1896?

537. How many English popes have there been?

538. In the Royal Air Force what is the rank above Wing Commander?

539. How many cells are there in a human body?

540. What is the capital of West Germany?

541. Which actor has written his autobiography entitled '*The Moon's a Balloon*'?

542. What is the single word used as the international radio distress call?

543. Which country left the Commonwealth in 1972?

544. Which month is named after a Roman emperor?

545. What French words are meant by the abbreviation R.S.V.P.?

546. Who was Penelope married to in Greek mythology?

547. What was the original name of the Russian city Leningrad?

548. What is the 'ship of the desert'?

549. What did Inigo Jones, John Nash and Le Corbusier have in common?

550. What is a simile?

551. What is a Joule?

552. Which English naturalist was the first to state a theory of evolution?

553. Where in the world is the area called the pampas?

554. As A is for Alfa, B for Bravo, C for Charlie, what is T for?

555. For what purpose do you use a metronome?

556. What is a ship's kitchen called?

557. Which American tennis player won nineteen titles between 1961 and 1975?

558. Who received the first transatlantic radio signals transmitted from his station in Cornwall?

559. Who was the French detective created by Georges Simenon?

560. How many sensations of taste do we have?

561. What is the first of the Ten Commandments?

562. What does Electronic Random Number Indicator Equipment do?

563. Which country has the longest individual railway?

564. Where in England is the National Motor Museum?

565. What do you buy in quires and reams?

566. What is the name of the last letter in the Greek alphabet, the opposite of Alpha?

567. Where would you find the *Arc de Triomphe?*

568. What is the O.E.D.?

569. What was the name of the Swiss hero who shot an apple on his son's head?

256

570. How many Deadly Sins are there?

571. In which European country do the Walloons live?

572. Who is the Duke of Cornwall?

573. In which country would you find a town called Vancouver?

574. What is a pomegranate?

575. Which English king won the battle of Agincourt in 1415?

576. Who was President of the USA during the Cuban crisis of 1962?

577. What part of your body is the aorta?

578. Where is the Cape of Good Hope?

579. What was the name of Napoleon's empress?

580. From which animal is veal obtained?

581. From which country did the Dalai Lama flee in 1959?

582. Which English aristocrat invented the boxing rules that bear his name?

583. What is a quadruped?

584. What do many people in China and south-east Asia use for eating their food?

585. What was the name of the English judge who was famous for his savage sentences at the 'Bloody Assizes' of 1685?

586. Who did David kill with a sling?

587. Who was the Maid of Orleans?

588. Where is the Kremlin?

589. What is the name for people who do not eat meat?

590. What type of fruit is a Royal Sovereign?

591. Where does the Pope live?

592. Who was Homer?

593. What is housed in the Palace of Westminster?

594. Which town was emptied of rats and children by the Pied Piper?

595. What type of fruit is a Cox's Orange Pippin?

596. What is another name for Namibia?

597. Which religious movement was founded by John Wesley?

598. What was Bedlam?

599. Who painted the ceiling of the Sistine Chapel?

600. What do you measure when you are sounding?

601. What colour is indigo?

602. In which industry is China Clay used?

603. Who originally owned the books which formed the basis of the British Museum Library?

604. Who did Napoleon defeat at the battle of Austerlitz in 1805?

605. What is a stickleback?

606. When is St. Valentine's Day?

607. Who was the Queen of the British tribe, the Iceni, who fought a guerrilla war against the Romans in 61 A.D.

608. What is a firkin?

609. What is the first day of Lent?

610. Who was warned, 'Beware the Ides of March'?

611. What is meerschaum used to make?

612. Which European country was invaded by the Moors in 711?

613. What is given an octane number?

614. What is amber?

615. Which small animal is trained to hunt rats and rabbits?

616. In which country is the Schilling the unit of currency?

617. What is a yak?

618. In which country is Thanksgiving Day celebrated on the fourth Thursday in November?

619. What was Telstar?

620. What is a zither?

621. What metal is used to make the filaments of electric light bulbs?

622. Where would you go to find Brooklyn, the Bronx and Manhattan?

623. What is neoprene?

624. When is St. Stephen's Day?

625. Where are the Elgin Marbles?

263

626. Who wears a mitre?

627. In which African country did the Mau-Mau movement arise?

628. What is a group of badgers called?

629. From what source is turpentine obtained?

630. What is the name of the animal that is protected by long, sharp spikes that cover its body?

631. What did Thomas Jefferson, Andrew Jackson, Woodrow Wilson and Harry Truman have in common?

632. What are studied in the science of palaeontology?

264

633. Which gas has the symbol H?

634. Where are epaulettes worn?

635. What are tsunamis often called incorrectly?

636. Which is the only poisonous snake native to the British Isles?

637. What evergreen plant was sacred to the Druids?

638. What kind of creature is a lamprey?

639. In which country do ladies wear kimonos?

640. What is the language invented by a Pole to be used as a form of international communication?

641. What was the famous survey of land and property in England commissioned by William the Conqueror?

642. What is the part of a horse's bridle worn in the horse's mouth.

643. In which American state would you find the cities of San Francisco and Los Angeles?

644. What is a grotto?

645. What was the earliest pre-historic bird called?

646. What does Hi-Fi mean?

647. What is a Jack Russell?

648. What is an amphibian?

649. What is another name for a panther?

650. Where was Napoleon Bonaparte born?

651. What is produced as a result of desalinisation?

652. What is a coracle?

653. What street in London is famous for newspapers?

654. What is another name for the chess piece called a castle?

655. What is a terrapin?

656. How many rowing decks were there in triremes?

657. Who is the patron Saint of Ireland?

658. Butane is one type of gas which is easily portable in a liquefied form. Can you name another common one?

659. Who lived in ancient Peru?

660. What is a deluge?

661. What is another term for an antenna?

662. From which Latin word does the word 'fossil' come from?

663. What event is commemorated by
the Monument of London?

664. Who was the most famous King of
the Huns from 406 to 453?

665. What is a truffle used for?

666. Which is the largest living bird?

667. From what is molasses extracted?

668. Why is Sir John Betjeman famous?

669. What is the Sunday before Easter
called?

670. What was the Louvre in Paris
before it was converted into a
museum?

671. What is a micrometer used for?

672. Which island is associated with sages?

673. Who used to carry the title, the Dauphin?

674. Where is Swahili spoken?

675. Which is the earth's smallest continent?

676. What is Big Ben?

677. What is a fresco?

678. What do the initials G.M.T. stand for?

679. Which building besides the River Thames was once a royal residence and has a famous maze?

680. Which Asian country were Olympic hockey champions from 1928 until 1960?

681. What would you study if you were an ornithologist?

682. In music what effect does a dot have on a note when it is placed after it?

683. What is the scientific name for the fear of being shut in?

684. Who sailed to America in the '*Mayflower*'?

685. How many muscles do you use to frown?

686. Which town on the Mediterranean coast of France holds a famous film festival every year?

687. With what campaign is the name of Mrs. Pankhurst associated?

688. Where in the body do sufferers of migraine feel the pain?

689. In which country did golf originate?

690. Where is the Grand Canyon?

691. To whom was Shakespeare's character Desdemona married?

692. Which country is referred to by the initials DDR?

693. On what day in the year are
pancakes traditionally eaten?

694. What was the title of the ruler of
Persia?

695. Where was the 'Six-Day War' of
1967 fought?

696. If someone refers to a Ming vase,
what do they mean?

697. How does a catamaran differ from
other sailing craft?

698. Why is Joseph Lister remembered
in the history of medicine?

699. Which English composer wrote the
'*Enigma Variations*'?

700. Who is 'Old Nick'?

701. Who travel in Black Marias?

702. What are monsoons?

703. Who painted the famous painting called '*The Last Supper*'?

704. Two English kings died in 1066. King Harold was one of them, who was the other?

705. What is a lute?

706. Which of the armed services has the motto 'Per Ardua Ad Astra'?

707. Where is poteen drunk?

708. Which US naval base was attacked by Japanese aircraft in December 1941, starting a war between the two countries?

709. Which English king invented the candle clock?

710. Where are the Needles?

711. In ancient Greece which mountain was believed to be the home of the gods?

712. Which operetta by Gilbert and Sullivan is named after the emperor of Japan?

713. What lies at the centre of the earth?

714. How long is a millenium?

715. What have drachma, zloty, guilder and lek in common?

716. What type of tree has leaves all the year round?

717. In which country is the Sinn Fein a political party?

718. What weapons were used by archers?

719. To what part of the body does the adjective 'nasal' refer?

720. If you send someone to Coventry what happens to him?

721. What is the official language in Israel?

722. What is produced in a fast breeder reactor?

723. Who became Queen of Egypt in 51 B.C.?

724. Which member of the ape family is thought to be closest to man?

725. Two German brothers wrote fairy tales in the early nineteenth century. Who were they?

726. How does a python kill its prey?

727. What is the name of the long thin country that runs along the east coast of South America?

728. What does a dynamo do?

729. Which bird is associated with the birth of children?

730. In which country would you find the cities of Haifa, Tel Aviv and Jerusalem?

731. What type of weapon was the Gatling Gun?

732. For how many years do you have to be married to celebrate your silver wedding anniversary?

733. What is the name given to wandering tribes with no permanent homes?

734. What is *pelota*?

735. Where do the Gurkhas come from?

736. How many countries are there in South America?

737. What landmark stands at the mouth of New York harbour?

738. Who wrote the stories about Peter Rabbit?

739. What did Rubens, Titian, Goya and Gauguin have in common?

740. In which sport is the expression 'a yorker' used?

741. What do you do with a hookah?

742. Who was the famous Greek writer of fables about animals?

743. How many pennies were there in the old British shilling?

744. The Koran is a sacred book of which religion?

745. What shape is a lateen sail?

746. What do we call the state in which animals spend the winter in a deep sleep?

747. Which great Asian river flows from the Himalayas across the plains of India and into the Bay of Bengal near Calcutta?

748. On which great American river would you find the city of New Orleans?

749. Which mythical bird is depicted rising out of smouldering ashes?

750. Who started the famous waxworks in London?

751. In which country is the world's most famous bicycle race held every year?

752. What type of meat is the principal export from New Zealand?

753. What word is used to describe the rules and customs of courtly behaviour of medieval knights?

754. Who carved and erected totem poles?

755. What land mass used to be known as the 'Dark Continent'?

756. Where do people describe stagnant backwaters as 'billabongs'?

757. Which lake in Scotland is famous for the monster that is believed to live in its depths?

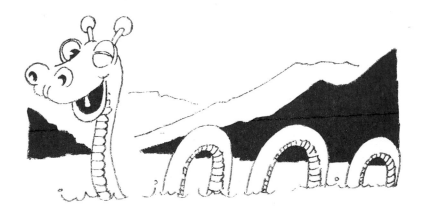

758. In order to be a true 'cockney' you have to be born within the sound of which peal of bells in London?

759. What are those spectacles called that have divided lenses for reading and normal vision?

760. What do you do to a ship or boat when you caulk it?

761. What do people do with incense?

762. What are stratus, cumulus and nimbus?

763. Who was Robin Hood constantly fighting against?

764. Only one part of Britain was captured by Germany during the Second World War. Which part was it?

765. Who went to Valhalla after their deaths?

766. Who wrote the play called '*The Mousetrap*'?

767. Which animal is unable to stick out its tongue?

768. Which animal in folklore has a single horn growing from its forehead?

769. What was robbed in 1963 when about £3,000,000 of used bank notes were stolen in England?

770. What is the name of the part of Rome where the Pope lives and rules?

771. Which capital city has a statue of a mermaid in its harbour?

772. In which continent is the Simpson Desert?

773. Who were called, 'A nation of shopkeepers'?

774. Which old English coin was commonly called 'a tanner'?

775. Where in Europe is the International Court of Justice?

776. Which city is associated with the wearing of togas?

777. What instrument is used to measure atmospheric pressure?

778. To whom do all the swans on the Thames belong?

779. Helium is a gas used in balloons because it does not burn. Which is the other gas, which does burn, that used to be used in balloons?

780. What do the British call what the Americans call a billion?

781. Which two countries are divided by the 49th Parallel?

782. What is produced by the lines of the fibres in wood?

783. What is a bison?

784. In which country did the Boxer Rebellion take place?

785. In which ocean is the Gulf Stream?

786. What is a kayak?

787. What was the Stuka?

788. What do we call the objects that sometimes crash into the earth's surface from Outer Space?

789. What is the 'cornea'?

790. Who was the German head of state during the First World War?

791. Which country is the setting for the film '*Zulu*'?

792. What do you have to be in order to belong to MENSA?

793. What was the strong tower at the centre of medieval castles called?

794. How can you identify a cow?

795. What did John Logie Baird invent?

796. Who created the Metropolitan Police force?

797. What do you have if you have 'the gift of the gab'?

798. When does a ship hoist the Blue Peter?

799. What is a pongo?

800. What are Sirius, Capella, Pollux and Canopus?

801. What colour is a turquoise?

802. Who was the first Secretary-General of the United Nations?

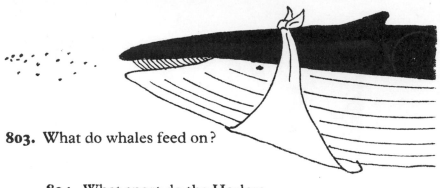

803. What do whales feed on?

804. What sport do the Harlem
Globetrotters play?

805. Which famous tunnel joins France
and Italy?

806. Which English king was called the
Lion Heart?

807. What is 'General Sherman'?

808. What are kept in an aviary?

809. How many cents are there in an
American dollar?

810. Which animal can turn its stomach
inside out?

811. What is the name for two children
that are born joined together?

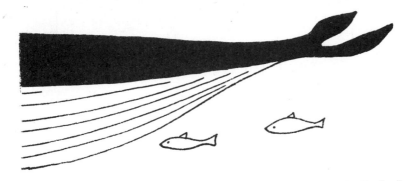

812. What is the capital of Canada?

813. Which of Captain Scott's companions sacrificed his own life in order to allow his comrades to move faster to safety?

814. What is jet?

815. Which South American animal resembles a leopard in appearance?

816. What is Harvard?

817. What kind of animals were Lassie and Rin Tin Tin?

818. Who had forty thieves?

819. For what event in British history is Guy Fawkes remembered?

820. Which religion celebrates the Feast of the Passover?

821. Which science is indebted to the work of Copernicus?

822. What country did Abel Tasman discover?

823. Snoopy has a bird-friend. What's his name?

824. What is the head-dress called that is made from a long piece of cloth wrapped around the head?

825. Which is the oldest university in England?

826. In which country was Mah Jong first played?

827. What animals are used in equestrian sports?

828. What is Gaelic?

829. What was the method of execution used during the French Revolution?

830. Which author wrote stories about Prince Caspian?

831. At night ships display coloured lights on each side to indicate which way they are pointing. What is the colour displayed on the port side?

832. Oil and natural gas are both fossil fuels. What is the other main one?

833. How many players are there in each team in a game of American football?

834. What is sisal used to make?

835. Which country is associated with windmills, tulips, clogs and cheese?

836. For what is Broadway in New York city famous?

837. Which bird has a reputation for stealing bright objects like jewellery?

838. If you undergo traction what happens to you?

839. Who were the Huguenots?

840. What musical instrument is associated with Scotland?

841. With which sport were the names Sonny Liston, Floyd Paterson, Jack Dempsey and Rocky Marciano once associated?

842. Of which country was Charlemagne once ruler?

843. If you hit the bull's eye what have you done?

844. What is the Old Bailey?

845. In which of Coleridge's poems does an albatross appear?

846. Seaweed is used to make many products. Can you think of 4?

847. What is jade?

848. Where would you wear a Tam-o-shanter?

849. What was Harry Houdini famous for?

850. What was papyrus used for?

851. What large black and white animal is only found wild in China?

852. What are the periods of duty on board ship called?

853. Where do cars with the registration letters DK come from?

854. In which sport is the Davis Cup an important trophy?

855. Which vitamin is contained in orange juice?

856. Which of the world's opera houses has a roof that resembles boats sailing in the nearby harbour?

857. If you are an octogenarian, how old are you?

858. What is Princess Anne's husband called?

859. Aeroflot is the national airline of which country?

860. What is a running bowline?

861. What is a tumulus?

862. What do anglers do?

863. Which is the largest member of the ape family?

864. Who uses a stethoscope?

865. What monument stands in Whitehall, in London?

866. In which South American country do many of the women wear bowler hats?

867. What does a taxidermist do?

868. How can you tell the age of a tree?

869. Who were the first to play lacrosse?

870. Who was the legendary Queen of Carthage who fell in love with Aeneas?

871. Where do bees make their honey?

872. What is Brie?

873. In which direction does a Moslem face when he prays?

874. What is normally kept on the lectern in a church?

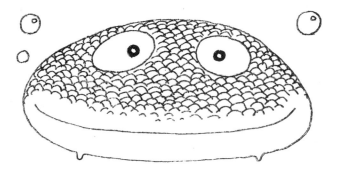

875. What type of fish is a conger?

876. Which common household appliances contain cathode ray tubes?

877. What day of the week is the Jewish Sabbath?

878. What animal is depicted in white on the side of the chalk hill at Uffington, in the Berkshire Downs?

879. Can you complete the proverb, 'Out of the frying pan into . . .'?

880. Which secret agent was first played by Sean Connery?

881. Which tree has a fireproof bark?

882. What are Leo, Pisces, Virgo and Aquarius?

883. What is the capital of Nigeria?

884. In what industry is a clapper-board used?

885. Where do you get dandruff?

886. What is the Three A's in sport?

887. If you performed an Eskimo Roll, what would you have done?

888. Which husband and wife scientific team discovered radium?

889. Which bird lays its eggs in the nests of other birds?

890. In which country is the religion Shinto practised?

891. Which country is the largest gold producer in the world?

892. Where would you find your
duodenum?

893. From which animal does venison
come?

894. What type of fungus is used in
breadmaking?

895. What is wanderlust?

896. Which American singing group
belong to the Mormon faith?

897. What was the name of the famous
oracle in Greece which the Greeks
called the centre of the earth?

898. What was the nationality of the
writer Hans Christian Andersen?

899. With which musical instrument do
you associate Yehudi Menuhin?

900. What is another name for the device
in a car called the throttle?

901. What nuts are used to make marzipan?

902. According to the song, what did 'my true love' bring me on the first day of Christmas?

903. What was Toledo famous for making during the Middle Ages?

904. How many tentacles has an octopus?

905. What is TNT?

906. Where are the English Crown Jewels kept?

907. From where is pumice stone obtained?

908. What kind of people meet at the World Jamboree?

909. What is an F.R.S.?

910. What are the larvae of flies that fishermen frequently use as bait?

911. What do diamonds and coal have in common?

912. Which national flag shows a red disc set on a white background?

913. Are sponges animals or plants?

914. Who invented the hovercraft?

915. Where are pearls found?

916. Where was the first four minute mile run?

917. Who is the patron saint of Wales?

918. Dr. Thomas Arnold was headmaster of which school?

919. What is the Cortes?

920. Bridge is the name of a game. What kind of game?

921. Where in the human body is the cerebrum?

922. What does the Beaufort scale measure?

923. A great American city was once called New Amsterdam. What is it called today?

924. Which planet lies further from the Sun in our Solar System?

925. Where would you wear a tiara?

926. Which famous building was erected in London to house the Great Exhibition of 1851?

927. What was a pterosaur?

928. What is produced by churning milk?

929. Where did the Silk Routes lead from?

930. Which American general was killed at the battle of Little Big Horn, his last stand?

931. What is a barque?

932. Who is elected by a conclave?

933. How many colours are there in a rainbow?

934. The fins of one type of fish are made into a soup. Which fish is it?

935. What are plus-fours?

936. What system of writing survives on Egyptian monuments?

937. Who was the first Plantagenet King of England?

938. The croup, the hock, the stifle and the gaskin are the names of parts of the body of a four-legged animal. Which one?

939. Which of the planets is characterised by a great red spot?

940. What type of music did Louis Armstrong play?

941. How many players are there in a rugger team?

942. What is a primula?

943. The lion is the symbol of England. What is the symbol of France?

944. What is the highest point on the African continent?

945. What is the everyday name for a solution of acetic acid?

946. What is the capital of the Irish Republic?

947. In which ancient Greek city is the Lion Gate still preserved?

948. Who is the Speaker of the House of Lords?

949. What does the Latin expression 'in toto' mean?

950. What is the scientific study of plants called?

951. What is kept in the sump of an engine?

952. What have Genesis, Isiah and Exodus in common?

953. What mineral is put into the ground by lightning?

954. Where would you possibly see a leprechaun?

955. What do the initials U.H.F. stand for?

956. What are bones held together with in our bodies?

957. How many feet has an animal that is a biped?

958. Do stalactites grow up or down?

959. Whose face is said to have launched a thousand ships?

960. What are the lines on which music is written?

961. In which sport is the Lonsdale belt awarded?

962. Which animal is connected with the legend of the founding of Rome.

963. From which French coastal resort was the British Expeditionary Force evacuated in 1940?

964. Which overture by Tchaikovsky has a date as its title?

965. In which country is the Suez Canal?

966. Who was Abel's brother?

967. What is measured in decibels?

968. Which famous composer was deaf for much of his working life?

969. Where is Afrikaans spoken?

970. Which nation was led by Genghis Khan?

971. What type of animal produces Cashmere wool?

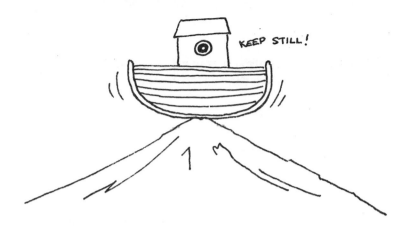

972. Which biblical ship came to rest on top of Mount Ararat?

973. Is the curve like the outside of a circle concave or convex?

974. Who would use a cleaver—a butcher, a baker or a candle-stick maker?

975. To which animal family does the cheetah belong?

976. Where was gunpowder first used?

977. How did Dick Turpin make his living?

978. When is the Feast of Saint Stephen?

979. What material is used to make the plaster cast in which broken bones can set?

980. Who was Galileo Galilei?

981. At what speed are long playing records normally played?

982. Fidel Castro is head of state of which country?

983. When did England last win the World Cup for football?

984. With which other country did Britain build Concorde?

985. What did Johann Gutenberg invent in about 1455?

986. What nationality was Mozart?

987. What is the title of the novel about rabbits by Richard Adams?

988. Which is the longest desert in the world?

989. In which Canadian province is the city of Vancouver?

990. What caused the death of at least a quarter of the people in Europe in 1348?

991. What did James Watt invent?

992. What are White Dwarfs and Red Giants?

993. What would you do with an
avocado?

994. What does Peter Sellers do for a
living?

995. What is another name for the game
of ping-pong?

996. Whose dying words were 'Kiss me
Hardy'?

997. Which metal is often used as a
roofing material because it is easy to
bend?

998. What is the capital of New Zealand?

999. With which sport is Jack Nicklaus
associated?

1000. What does the Latin word *finis* mean?

1000 ANSWERS

1. Eight   2. The science of the study of rocks
3. Albert   4. Carthaginian   5. Pisa
6. Blessed Virgin Mary   7. Canada
8. The Duke of Wellington   9. The Blue Whale
10. Sir Walter Raleigh   11. Henry V
12. Glenn Miller   13. Sir Christopher Wren
14. Greenland (Australia is really a continent)
15. 144   16. Marco Polo   17. The Seine
18. None—he was a playwright!
19. Queen Victoria   20. In North Africa
21. The Marx Brothers   22. Mohammed
23. National Aeronautics and Space Administration
24. 1947   25. Eleven   26. Handel
27. In Canterbury Cathedral   28. Edwin Aldrin
29. The Cyrillic script   30. 'Casablanca'
31. Mark Twain
32. At the southern tip of South America
33. It is a Canadian Province
34. Criminal Investigation Department
35. Bogotá   36. King Alfred
37. Salzburg, in Austria   38. Mulberry leaves
39. On the side of a ship   40. Samuel Pepys
41. Two   42. Antonine's Wall
43. Feeding on all kinds of food   44. A quart
45. Seven   46. Charles Lindberg
47. The Great Pyramid of Cheops
48. The Beatles   49. French   50. Sherpa Tenzing
51. The femur or thigh bone   52. Icarus
53. The rouble   54. Iron   55. The Bible
56. Michelangelo   57. A pride   58. Mardi Gras
59. Oscar Wilde
60. In south-west Europe, near the Pyrenees
61. The Amazon   62. A dried and cured herring

315

63. The Moon   64. Egypt   65. Charles Dickens
66. Greek
67. Treats injuries by manipulating bones
68. Trafalgar Square   69. Clark Kent   70. London
71. King George VI   72. Yuri Gagarin   73. White
74. Cambodia
75. A German airship at the beginning of the century
76. Salyut   77. In Venezuela   78. A female fox
79. 1000   80. Alexander Graham Bell
81. On the Isle of Man   82. Spanish
83. 'The Golden Hind'
84. Chou En-lai and Mao Tse Tung
85. 'My Fair Lady'   86. Salisbury   87. Marriage
88. As a ballet dancer   89. Jupiter
90. The woodwind   91. West Germany
92. Louis XVI   93. Fred Perry   94. Turin
95. John Milton   96. Leg before wicket
97. In the ear   98. Lyndon B. Johnson
99. Portuguese   100. A type of kangaroo
101. The Hellespont
102. Neither. They weigh the same   103. Six
104. Kon-Tiki   105. Treats the hands and feet
106. Moses   107. Venus
108. He was the 7th United States President
109. Bauxite   110. Los Angeles   111. He was a poet
112. Alaska   113. A human being   114. King John
115. San Salvador   116. Single lens reflex
117. Camelot   118. Olive Oyl   119. Hinduism
120. Thumper   121. Mont Blanc   122. An elephant
123. Wind speed   124. Mercury
125. The Penny Black   126. Navigation
127. Orville and Wilbur Wright
128. Catherine of Aragon   129. Richard Wagner
130. Mount Etna   131. The badger
132. In northern Scandinavia
133. Oxygen and Hydrogen (H_2O)   134. On the left

135. The spinal cord   **136.** Hamlet   **137.** 1980

138. Cheese   **139.** The albatross

140. A method of signalling using the arms

141. *'Butch Cassidy and the Sundance Kid'*

142. Gauchos   **143.** Sir Henry Morton Stanley

144. Double Eagle II

145. Unidentified Flying Object   **146.** A butterfly

147. At a wedding   **148.** A gambling game

149. Julius Caesar   **150.** Leonardo da Vinci

151. The Central Intelligence Agency

152. Horatio Nelson   **153.** St. Brendan's

154. St. Christopher   **155.** A strong rough cider

156. Uranium   **157.** Liza Minnelli   **158.** The pig

159. Waterways and canals

160. Richard Rodgers and Oscar Hammerstein

161. A giant, flightless bird, now extinct

162. The Danish Flag

163. At No. 10 Downing Street

164. Alexandre Gustave Eiffel   **165.** −40° Centigrade

166. Remus   **167.** An eight angled or eight sided figure

168. Robin   **169.** At Agra, India   **170.** *'The Titanic'*

171. Saigon

172. The *Marseillaise* is the French national anthem. Mayonnaise is salad dressing!

173. Mark well   **174.** The accused   **175.** Uganda

176. The Organisation of Petroleum Exporting Countries

177. Drums   **178.** Sir Arthur Conan Doyle

179. The Richter Scale   **180.** The United States

181. The Soviet Union   **182.** The White Ensign

183. Lord Baden-Powell   **184.** New York

185. Alfred Nobel   **186.** Thomas Gainsborough

187. S.O.S.   **188.** After the Latin number 'novem' ('nine'), it was the ninth month of the Roman calendar

189. Green cheese   **190.** A gaggle   **191.** John Curry

192. The George Cross   **193.** The Bayeux Tapestry

194. Drum brakes   195. Operation Overlord
196. Cambridge and Oxford   197. The Boeing 747
198. Charon   199. The Victory   200. Bhutan
201. The aborigines
202. She was Prime Minister of India
203. Geneva   204. Ottawa
205. The local name given to the 'Abominable
     Snowman' in the Himalayas
206. General Gordon   207. F.D. Roosevelt
208. The River Severn
209. A hot spring which shoots steam into the air
210. A circle   211. The Prince of Wales   212. Acorns
213. Georges Pompidou
214. The Royal Shakespeare Company
215. Surinam   216. The characters in a play
217. Gustave Holst   218. Alexei Leonov   219. Canvas
220. Animals which carry their young in pouches
221. Charlie Chaplin   222. James Hunt
223. The Panther 6 224. Constantinople 225. Vodka
226. St. Nicholas or Father Christmas
227. District of Columbia   228. Roger Moore
229. He was an explorer and navigator
230. Enid Blyton 231. Suffragettes 232. Friar Tuck
233. The Rhine   234. A large bird of prey
235. The Pacific
236. A game like hockey played on horseback
237. Roman   238. The Plague
239. Neville Chamberlain   240. The Harrier
241. A cygnet   242. Islamabad   243. Saturn
244. The cow   245. A nautical mile   246. Twelve
247. In China   248. Jane   249. Calypso or Reggae
250. Locomotion No. 1   251. He is an actor
252. Yugoslavia 253. In Brazil 254. 144
255. Ian Fleming
256. The type of rain that falls during thunderstorms
257. The puck   258. An ignition system

259. Legions   260. Prince Rainier of Monaco
261. Robert Louis Stephenson   262. The Dead Sea
263. Mountain   264. In New York city
265. A dictionary   266. Richard III
267. Micky Mouse   268. Greenwich Mean Time
269. Cirrus   270. Thousandfold
271. Across San Francisco harbour
272. The day before Good Friday
273. A hand game, similar to Squash   274. Boston
275. The mackerel   276. Exodus
277. Benito Mussolini   278. A one-humped camel
279. Designing and making furniture
280. The cos lettuce   281. Lockjaw
282. A unit of currency   283. Harris
284. The storming of the Bastille—said to mark
     the beginning of the French Revolution
285. 47   286. Rats   287. In Washington D.C.
288. A dinosaur   289. Robinson Crusoe   290. Salt
291. Egypt   292. The horse   293. Peter the Great
294. The Black Hole   295. Solomon   296. Cricket
297. The Peseta   298. The pike   299. Pompeii
300. Sir Barnes Wallis   301. Winds
302. The Tower of London   303. 11th November
304. Mars   305. The Penny-Farthing   306. Funny
307. As Buffalo Bill 308. In Australia 309. Gnomes
310. As an engineer   311. Paper
312. You lose your memory   313. Louis Blériot
314. Killing a King   315. Frankincense
316. The Marathon   317. The Jolly Roger
318. In the eye
319. Household management and cooking
320. South Africa   321. Thirty-nine   322. Edward
323. Radioactivity   324. The sturgeon
325. Abraham Lincoln   326. The Balaclava helmet
327. Prehistoric rock paintings   328. Julius Caesar
329. K.2.   330. In Egypt   331. King Arthur

332. In Babylon   **333.** In mountainous areas
334. From Paris   **335.** Ludwig van Beethoven
336. Fourteen   **337.** The Archbishop of Canterbury
338. Hercule Poirot   **339.** A colony   **340.** A massacre
341. St. Peter's, in Rome   **342.** Five   **343.** Norwegian
344. Dr. Samuel Johnson   **345.** His strength
346. Alaska   **347.** Lawrence of Arabia   **348.** A lama
349. On ice   **350.** Mr. Bhutto   **351.** 121   **352.** Heat
353. In mosques   **354.** Niccolo Machiavelli
355. At the mouths of rivers   **356.** The elephant
357. Henry VIII   **358.** Part of a sheep's stomach
359. Constellations
360. Solving mathematical problems
361. Sir Arthur Sullivan   **362.** Calcium
363. The Emperor Nero   **364.** Cash on delivery
365. In South Africa   **366.** Sir Francis Chichester
367. A ram   **368.** In Jerusalem   **369.** Draw maps
370. A professor of English literature
371. On the island of Crete   **372.** Hockey
373. In Nazareth   **374.** In Wiltshire, Great Britain
375. S.N.C.F.   **376.** Cherries
377. Working with rope   **378.** A school
379. The stick insect   **380.** Bobsledding
381. Eric the Red   **382.** On the island of Rhodes
383. Rabbit   **384.** A successful gardener
385. Measure time with great accuracy   **386.** A pistol
387. Three   **388.** The bunsen burner   **389.** One
390. Contour lines   **391.** 84   **392.** In a desert
393. In Australia   **394.** In Edinburgh   **395.** 1984
396. A carpenter
397. Spaghetti does not grow, it is manufactured
398. Oranges   **399.** Mercury   **400.** Mecca
401. The left side looking towards the bows
402. Insurance   **403.** Madagascar
404. Florence Nightingale   **405.** 100
406. The Silver Jubilee of Queen Elizabeth II

407. Polish   408. Peter Pan   409. A dinner jacket
410. The kiwi   411. Eucalyptus
412. She was the first woman in space
413. Federal Bureau of Investigation
414. Goose livers   415. Red   416. Ceylon
417. King of the Norse gods   418. Boxing
419. Alcock and Brown   420. Russian
421. The Cullinan Diamond
422. In Sarajevo, Yugoslavia
423. Field-Marshal Erwin Rommel
424. Between the engine and the gearbox
425. Paddington   426. The Tynwald   427. Edward
428. France   429. Carbon monoxide   430. Gills
431. A mallet   432. Czechoslovakia   433. Damascus
434. Forty days   435. Tokyo   436. Jules Verne
437. Germany   438. Jacques Cousteau   439. Cantons
440. Saint Andrew   441. Ivory   442. San Francisco
443. King Canute   444. Psalm 119
445. Anne and Charlotte   446. Arizona
447. Badminton   448. Jack Ruby
449. St. Francis of Assisi   450. India   451. A hare
452. Ireland   453. A nappy   454. Coffee
455. John Lennon and Paul McCartney of the Beatles
456. Teeth   457. Copper and tin   458. An altimeter
459. The Lord Chancellor   460. In a castle
461. A vegetable   462. Arthur Miller
463. Denmark   464. Thigh bone
465. Value Added Tax   466. Dr. Henry Kissinger
467. Out-of-doors   468. A dance   469. Green
470. Bill Haley and the Comets   471. Venice
472. Sancho Panza   473. Stockholm
474. 'The Lusitania'   475. The giraffe   476. Finland
477. Thomas Alva Edison
478. You become drowsy and often fall asleep
479. Musical notes   480. Switzerland
481. The Braille system   482. The Black Sea

483. On its back
484. British Broadcasting Corporation
485. The starboard side   486. 360
487. The model T Ford   488. The Mosquito
489. Cape Kennedy   490. Fifty years   491. Austrian
492. Penicillin   493. Chalk   494. £20
495. Furniture   496. 1 March
497. Tim Rice and Andrew Lloyd Webber
498. Painting   499. He's a conductor   500. MDIX
501. A large prehistoric animal   502. Easter island
503. Graphite   504. All four were composers
505. Motor-cycles   506. In convents   507. Seaweed
508. William the Conqueror
509. The Distinguished Service Cross
510. Macbeth   511. The Chinese in A.D.700
512. Brandy   513. Nitrogen
514. The study of old age   515. Mohammed Ali
516. Ajax (Amsterdam)   517. Holyhead   518. D
519. Merlin   520. In Scapa Flow   521. A knot
522. The Pacific Ocean   523. The Tropic of Cancer
524. Yew trees   525. Tintin   526. Autumn
527. Krakatoa, in Indonesia   528. Shannon
529. A spider   530. In the Caribbean
531. One light-year   532. Her Majesty the Queen
533. 'Love Me Do'   534. Revolutions per minute
535. Stringed instruments   536. In Athens   537. One
538. Group Captain   539. About 60,000,000,000,000
540. Bonn   541. David Niven   542. 'Mayday'
543. Pakistan   544. August, after Augustus Caesar
545. Répondez s'il vous plait   546. Odysseus
547. St. Petersburg   548. The camel
549. All three were architects   550. A figure of speech
551. A unit of energy or work   552. Charles Darwin
553. In Argentina   554. Tango   555. Marking time
556. A galley   557. Mrs. Billie Jean King
558. Guglielmo Marconi   559. Inspector Maigret

560. 4-sweet, salt, sour and bitter
561. 'You shall have no other God to set against me'
562. Select winning Premium Bond numbers
563. Canada   564. In Beaulieu, Hampshire
565. Paper   566. Omega   567. In Paris
568. The Oxford English Dictionary
569. William Tell   570. Seven   571. In Belgium
572. The Prince of Wales   573. Canada
574. A fruit   575. Henry V
576. John F. Kennedy   577. The main artery
578. At the southern tip of Africa   579. Josephine
580. The calf   581. Tibet
582. The Marquis of Queensbury
583. A four-footed animal   584. Chopsticks
585. Judge Jeffreys   586. Goliath   587. Joan of Arc
588. In Moscow   589. Vegetarian   590. A strawberry
591. In the Vatican   592. An ancient Greek poet
593. The British parliament   594. Hamlyn
595. An apple   596. South-West Africa
597. Methodism   598. A lunatic asylum
599. Michelangelo   600. Depth, usually in the sea
601. Deep blue   602. The pottery industry
603. King George III
604. The Austrians and the Russians
605. A small, spiny-finned fish   606. 14 February
607. Boadicea   608. A small barrel
609. Ash Wednesday   610. Julius Caesar
611. Pipe-bowls   612. Spain   613. Petrol
614. Resin from prehistoric pine trees which has
      hardened over millions of years
615. The ferret   616. Austria
617. A long-haired ox found in the Himalayas
618. USA   619. The first television satellite
620. A musical instrument   621. Tungsten
622. New York   623. A type of synthetic rubber
624. 26 December   625. In the British Museum

626. A bishop   **627.** In Kenya   **628.** A cete

629. Coniferous trees   **630.** A porcupine

631. They were all Presidents of the United States

632. Fossils   **633.** Hydrogen   **634.** On the shoulders

635. Tidal waves   **636.** The adder   **637.** Mistletoe

638. A fish   **639.** Japan   **640.** Esperanto

641. Domesday Book   **642.** The bit

643. California   **644.** A cave

645. Archaeopteryx   **646.** High fidelity   **647.** A dog

648. An animal that can live both in water and on the land

649. A leopard   **650.** On Corsica   **651.** Pure water

652. A type of small boat   **653.** Fleet Street

654. A rook   **655.** A type of fresh-water tortoise

656. Three   **657.** St. Patrick   **658.** Propane

659. The Incas   **660.** A flood   **661.** An aerial

662. 'Fossilis' which means 'something dug up'

663. The Great Fire of London   **664.** Attila

665. Seasoning food   **666.** The ostrich

667. Sugar-cane

668. As Poet Laureate of Great Britain

669. Palm Sunday   **670.** A royal palace

671. Measuring very small distances   **672.** Iceland

673. The eldest son of the King of France

674. In many parts of Africa   **675.** Europe

676. The clock on the Houses of Parliament

677. A painting   **678.** Greenwich Mean Time

679. Hampton Court   **680.** India   **681.** Birds

682. It increases the length of the note by half as much again

683. Claustrophobia   **684.** The Pilgrim Fathers

685. 43   **686.** Cannes

687. The right of women to vote   **688.** In the head

689. Scotland   **690.** In Colorado, USA   **691.** Othello

692. East Germany   **693.** Shrove Tuesday

694. The Shah

695. In the Middle East, around Israel

696. A vase made in China during the Ming dynasty (1368–1644)

697. It has two hulls

698. He pioneered the use of antiseptics

699. Sir Edward Elgar **700.** The Devil

701. Prisoners in police custody.

702. Winds in south-east Asia

703. Leonardo da Vinci **704.** Edward the Confessor

705. A musical instrument

706. The Royal Air Force **707.** In Ireland

708. Pearl Harbor **709.** King Alfred

710. On the western extremity of the Isle of Wight

711. Mount Olympus **712.** 'The Mikado'

713. The core **714.** One thousand years

715. They are all units of currency

716. An evergreen **717.** In Ireland

718. Bows and arrows **719.** The nose

720. No one speaks to him **721.** Hebrew

722. Nuclear power **723.** Cleopatra

724. The chimpanzee **725.** The brothers Grimm

726. By crushing it **727.** Chile

728. Generates electricity **729.** The stork

730. Israel **731.** A machine gun **732.** Twentyfive

733. Nomads

734. A ball game played in Spain and the Basque country

735. Nepal **736.** Eleven **737.** The Statue of Liberty

738. Beatrix Potter **739.** All four were artists

740. Cricket **741.** Smoke tobacco through it

742. Aesop **743.** Twelve **744.** Islam **745.** Triangular

746. Hibernation **747.** The Ganges

748. The Mississippi **749.** The phoenix

750. Madame Tussaud **751.** In France

752. Lamb **753.** Chivalry **754.** American Indians

755. Africa **756.** In Australia **757.** Loch Ness

758. Bow bells   **759.** Bifocals
760. Makes its seams watertight   **761.** Burn it
762. Types of clouds
763. The Sheriff of Nottingham
764. The Channel Islands
765. Viking warriors killed in battle
766. Dame Agatha Christie   **767.** Crocodile
768. The unicorn   **769.** A train
770. The Vatican City   **771.** Copenhagen
772. Australia   **773.** The English
774. A sixpence   **775.** In the Hague   **776.** Rome
777. A barometer   **778.** The Crown   **779.** Hydrogen
780. A thousand million
781. Canada and the United States   **782.** The grain
783. A type of wild cattle   **784.** China
785. The Atlantic   **786.** A type of canoe
787. A German dive-bomber of the Second
    World War
788. Meteorites
789. The see-through section of the eye
790. The Kaiser   **791.** South Africa
792. Very intelligent   **793.** The keep
794. By making a 'fingerprint' of its nose
795. The television   **796.** Sir Robert Peel
797. The ability to speak well
798. Before leaving harbour   **799.** A kind of ape
800. The names of stars   **801.** Blue, or greenish blue
802. Trygve Lie   **803.** Plankton   **804.** Basketball
805. The Mont Blanc Tunnel   **806.** Richard I
807. The largest tree in the world, a sequoia pine,
    in California
808. Birds   **809.** 100   **810.** Starfish
811. Siamese twins   **812.** Ottawa
813. Lawrence Oates   **814.** A black fossil material
815. The jaguar
816. The name of an American university

817. Dogs   **818.** Ali Baba

819. The Gunpowder Plot   **820.** Judaism

821. Astronomy   **822.** Tasmania   **823.** Woodstock

824. A turban   **825.** Oxford   **826.** China

827. Horses   **828.** A Scottish and Irish language

829. The guillotine   **830.** C.S.Lewis   **831.** Red

832. Coal   **833.** Eleven   **834.** Ropes

835. The Netherlands   **836.** Theatres

837. The jackdaw

838. Part of your body is stretched

839. French protestants   **840.** The bagpipes

841. Boxing   **842.** France

843. Hit the centre of a target

844. The name of a court in London

845. The Rhyme of the Ancient Mariner

846. Paint, medicine, fertiliser, tooth-paste, ice-cream

847. A hard stone   **848.** On your head

849. Feats of escaping

850. Making the earliest form of paper

851. The panda   **852.** Watches   **853.** Denmark

854. Tennis   **855.** Vitamin C   **856.** Sydney

857. Between 80 and 89 years old

858. Captain Mark Phillips   **859.** The Soviet Union

860. A knot   **861.** A mound of earth   **862.** Go fishing

863. The gorilla   **864.** A doctor   **865.** The Cenotaph

866. Bolivia   **867.** He stuffs dead animals

868. By counting the number of rings in a cross-section

869. American Indians   **870.** In hives   **871.** Dido

872. A French cheese   **873.** Towards Mecca

874. The Bible   **875.** An eel   **876.** Television sets

877. Saturday   **878.** A White Horse

879. . . . the fire'   **880.** James Bond   **881.** Redwood

882. Four of the signs of the Zodiac   **883.** Lagos

884. The film industry   **885.** On the scalp

886. The Amateur Athletic Association
887. Righted a capsized canoe with a stroke of
the paddle
888. The Curies 889. The cuckoo 890. Japan
891. South Africa
892. Below your stomach: it is the first part of your
small intestine
893. The deer 894. Yeast 895. The love of travel
896. The Osmonds 897. Delphi 898. Danish
899. The violin 900. The accelerator 901. Almonds
902. 'A partridge in a pear tree' 903. Swords
904. Eight 905. An explosive
906. In the Tower of London
907. Volcanic lava flows 908. Scouts and Guides
909. A Fellow of the Royal Society 910. Maggots
911. Both are made of carbon 912. The Japanese flag
913. Animals 914. Christopher Cockerell
915. In the shells of some oysters 916. In Oxford
917. St. David 918. Rugby School
919. The Spanish Parliament 920. A card game
921. In the head. It is part of the brain
922. Wind speeds 923. New York 924. Pluto
925. On your head 926. The Crystal Palace
927. A prehistoric flying reptile 928. Butter
929. China 930. General Custer
931. A small sailing ship 932. The Pope
933. Seven 934. The shark 935. Kind of trousers
936. Hieroglyphics 937. Henry II 938. The horse
939. Jupiter 940. Jazz 941. Fifteen
942. A kind of flower 943. The cockerel
944. Mt. Kilimanjaro 945. Vinegar
946. Dublin 947. Mycenae
948. The Lord Chancellor 949. Entirely
950. Botany 951. Lubricating oil
952. All three are names of books in the
Old Testament of the Bible

953. Nitrogen **954.** In Ireland
955. Ultra High Frequency **956.** Ligaments
957. Two **958.** Down **959.** Helen of Troy's
960. Staves **961.** Boxing **962.** The wolf
963. Dunkirk **964.** The 1812 overture
965. In Egypt **966.** Cain
967. The loudness of sound
968. Ludwig van Beethoven **969.** In South Africa
970. The Mongols **971.** A goat **972.** Noah's Ark
973. Convex **974.** A butcher **975.** The cat family
976. In ancient China **977.** He was a highwayman
978. 26th December **979.** Plaster of Paris
980. He was an Italian mathematician
and astronomer
981. 33 r.p.m. **982.** Cuba **983.** In 1966
984. France **985.** The printing press
986. Austrian **987.** 'Watership Down' **988.** Sahara
989. British Columbia **990.** The Black Death
991. The steam engine **992.** Types of stars
993. Eat it : it is a fruit **994.** He is a film actor
995. Table tennis **996.** Horatio Nelson **997.** Lead
998. Wellington **999.** Golf **1000.** The end

PART THREE

1000
BRAINTEASERS

Here is a model for you to copy. Card is better than paper and once you've cut your set you can use it time and time again.

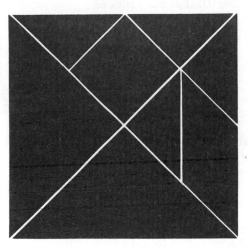

The important thing to remember with all these brainteasers is that you don't need to be a genius to enjoy them. If you're prepared to stretch your brain just a little, you're as likely to hit on the right answer as the Mastermind next door.

So on with your thinking caps and happy puzzling.

1. Using your 7 tangram pieces can you construct the number 1? (Remember to use all 7 pieces without any of them overlapping.) The figure should look like this:

2. This famous race-course is not on the **COAST**. What is its name?

3. What is the next number in this series: **1 3 4 6 7 9 . . .**

4. Fill in the missing letters to produce the right answer: **WxNxIx TxE xOxH**

5. Which piece of wood or plastic is most like a king?

6. How many grooves are there in a long-playing gramophone record?

7. If I set my alarm clock to wake me at 10.00 a.m. when I go to bed at 9.00 p.m., how many hours of sleep will I get before the alarm rings?

8. Look at these numbers and then tell the time: 5 4 3 2 1

9. Only one prime number is also an even number. Which is it?

10. These matches represent an equation. The answer shown here is wrong. If you move one match though you can correct it. Which match must you move?

11. Form this figure with your tangram pieces:

12. If my brother was **WARNED**, what is his name?

13. If a clock strikes six in 5 seconds, how long does it take to strike twelve?

14. Add an animal's coat to each of these groups of letters to form words: **LONG, NACE, ROW, THEST**

15. Why are pianos difficult to unlock?

16. *What is the beginning of eternity,*
The end of time and space,
The beginning of every end,
And the end of every race?

17. If tomorrow's today is Saturday, what is the day after tomorrow's yesterday?

18. What is the next number in this series: **1 2 3 2 5 4 9 8 17 16** . . . ?

19. Here are three clues to three words which each contain the same three letters. What are the letters and the words they make?

(a) A part of the body. **(b)** A farm animal.
(c) To spoil

20. Can you arrange nine dots to form ten rows of three dots?

21. Use your tangram pieces to form this shape:

22. There are eight apples in a bag and eight children who each want an apple. Is it possible to give an apple to each child and still end up with one in the bag?

23. Who caused the teacher
    to **SLIP-UP?**

24. He was a famous writer and
    his surname reminds you
    of Christmas singing.
    Who was he?

25. Which animal's eye gets
    hit the most?

26. Put two letters in front of **G L I C** and the same
    two letters behind to form an eight-letter word
    connected with the church.

27. If you have eight black socks in your drawer
    and eight white socks and you want to take out
    a pair in the dark without turning on the light,
    how many will you need to take out to be sure
    of having a pair?

28. What is the next number in this series: **1 3 9 27
    81 243. . . .?**

29. Which famous London sports ground has a
    name that reminds you of part of the British
    government?

30. Can you make **10** by using nine matches?

31. Make this shape with your tangram
    pieces:

32. Which type of cattle can you **DEHORN**?

33. Imagine that you are travelling on a train moving at 100 miles an hour. Now you jump two feet in the air. Where do you land?

34. Put a colour in front of these groups of letters to form words: **UCE, UNDANT, DEN, DISH**

35. Why are clocks shy?

36. A soldier standing to attention and facing west was given these orders: 'Right turn. About turn. Left turn. About turn.' Which direction was he facing at the end?

37. Can you think of the whole number which produces a greater answer when it is added to 10,000 than it does when 10,000 is multiplied by it?

38. If you are given five sweets and told that you can only eat one every half hour, what is the shortest time in which you can eat them all?

39. Fill in the missing letters to find a popular drink: **IxSxAxT xOxFxE**

40. A man looking at a portrait says:
'Sisters and brothers have I none,
But that man's father was my father's son.'

How is the speaker related to the man in the picture?

41. Make this shape with your tangram pieces:

42. Which floor in the tall building is quite a **HEIGHT**?

43. If a prime number (like 3, 5, 7 and 9) cannot be divided evenly by any other number, and a palindromic number is one which reads the same backwards as forwards, (like 121) what is the next palindromic prime number after 11?

44. Can you add the next two letters to this sequence? **TETWTHFOFISI** ...

45. What is pointed in one direction and headed in the other?

46. Imagine that you have seven marbles six of which weigh the same and one of which is lighter than the rest. Using just the marbles on a pair of scales how many times would you need to weigh them to find the light marble?

47. Which is the next number is this sequence: **1 3 6 11 18 27** ...?

48. Do you know a girl's name of six letters which is a palindrome (one that spells the same backwards as well as forwards)?

49. Which is heavier one tonne of steel or one tonne of balsa wood?

50. How many triangles are there in this diagram?

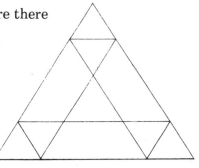

51. Use your tangram pieces to form this shape:

52. What would you need for something that **RECOOLS**?

53. Which is the odd one out in this sequence: **Eagle, pigeon, ostrich, swift, gull, robin?**

54. Fill in the missing letters to name this well-known landmark: **TxWxR xF xOxDxN**

55. Why isn't your nose twelve inches long?

56. One letter has been altered in each of the words in this proverb. Can you replace the correct letters to complete the proverb: Bake say whale tee sin chines?

57. Remove two matches from this pattern to leave three squares:

58. Can you arrange the numbers from 1 to 7 in a sum so that they will add up to 100?

59. Here are the names of two famous women jumbled together. Cross out groups of letters to find one name and reveal the other: **TH, EL, IZ, AT, AB, CH, ETH, ER**

60. Both these words begin with T. They sound the same but one is the name of a bird while the other is another way of describing a process of moving round. What are the words?

61. Use your tangram pieces to make this shape:

62. How would you describe your friend with the **THICKEST** body?

63. What is the next number in this series: **2 5 11 23 47 . . .?**

64. Fill in the missing letters to complete this famous baby's name: **PxIxCx WxLxIxM**

65. Which is faster hot or cold?

66. Can you spot the odd one out in this series: **Bermuda, Crete, Greenland, Denmark, Tasmania, Jamaica**

67. Add five more matches to these six to make nine:

68. If a father is 40 years old and his son is 13, how many years ago was the father four times older than his son?

69. A famous soldier is disguised here as **JELLIOUS SEE-SAW**. What is his real name?

70. This looks like a word in a foreign language but it's really the name of a well-known British landmark with a few of the letters missing. Replace them to complete the name: **HEPOTOFIETWER**

71. Use your tangram pieces to make this shape:

72. Which is the next letter in this sequence: **A C E G I K M O Q S U** ...?

73. Can you think of metal which, when read backwards, sounds like the name for a way of making clothes?

74. Where in the house would you hide to avoid the **CALLER** you don't want to see?

75. Why are flowers lazy?

76. One of these doesn't belong in this group. Can you spot it: **Pencil, biro, typewriter, word-processor, ruler, crayon**

77. Can you make four equilateral triangles with six matches?

78. What was the date of the first day of the twentieth century? Was it 1 January, 1900 or 1 January 1901?

79. If clocks struck the hours from 1 to 24 every hour, how many times would a clock strike in a 24-hour day?

80. Hidden in **UNSIGHTLY** is another word with a similar meaning. Can you find it?

81. Use your tangram pieces to make this shape:

82. When do you **SET-OUT** for a journey?

83. What is the next number in this sequence: **2 7 17 37 77** ...?

84. Find the answer to this clue and it will also give you another word which sounds the same but is spelt differently: Another word for pretty: **F ...? and F ...?**

85. What is dark but made by light?

86. Look at these two series of words. One word from the first series has found its way into the second. Which is it: **ape, chimpanzee, gorilla, orang-outang — pony, horse, gibbon, donkey**

87. Which is the longer of these two lines?
    Is it the horizontal line a to b,
    or the vertical line c to d?

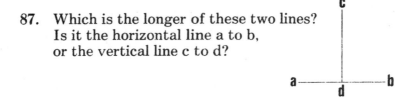

88. Which word is always spelt incorrectly?

89. A farmer walking his sheep to market was
    asked how many he had. The farmer replied,
    *'When they are walking in a line there are two
    sheep in front of a sheep, two sheep behind a
    sheep, and one sheep in the middle.'* How many
    sheep were there?

90. What do these all have in common: **Kennedy,
    Nixon, Carter, Lincoln, Washington?**

91. Use your tangram pieces
    to make this shape:

92. When you are walking over marshy ground
    where is it safest to **STRIDE?**

93. Lorna has more sweets than Judy or Sarah, but the same number as Linda, who has fewer than Mary. Which of the girls has the most sweets?

94. Can you think of a word to do with being strong that has nine letters but only one of which is a vowel?

95. There is one thing everyone in the world is doing at this moment, apart from living. What is that?

96. Draw a triangle like this. Carefully mark out the lines and then cut out the pieces along those lines. Now try and put the pieces back together to form a square.

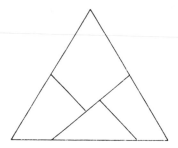

97. Spot the odd one out in this series: **catgut, stallion, toast, underdog, flying**

98. Believe it or not this is the name of a country. Study the letters, rearrange them and find which country it is: **Leenuvzea**

99. If $\frac{1}{4}$ of 16 is not 4 but 3, what should eleven forty-fourths of 16 be?

100. Inside this word is another word with a similar meaning: **OBSERVE**. What's the second word?

101. Use your tangram pieces to make this shape:

102. Where does a fisherman keep his **LOOPS** of line?

103. What are the next **three** numbers in this sequence: **1 3 5 7 9 11 13 . . .?**

104. Can you think of a word to do with motion which added to both 'up' and 'down' has the same meaning in both cases?

105. Which kind of pine has the sharpest needles?

106. One of the words from this first sequence is hidden in the second. Which is it? **Banana, pear, cherry, plum — cabbage, celery, date, cabbage, spinach**

107. Move two matches from this pattern and make seven squares:

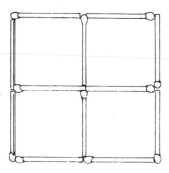

108. What is wrong with this sentence: Alfie is the tallest of the two brothers?

109. What do each of these have in common: **fork, spade, shovel, chisel, hammer, rake?**

110. These letters all stand for names. Where an 'x' appears there is another letter/name missing. Which are the missing letters?
J x M x M x J x S x N x

111. Use your tangram pieces to make this shape:

112. If you lived in Japan, what part of China would be **NEAREST**?

113. Look at this row of numbers and draw a circle round every group of three numbers that add up to 15: **3 1 4 1 5 9 2 6 5 2 5 8 3 5 7 9 7 9**

114. Can you correct this sentence: *The vicar red from a book of won of the profits in the Old Tenement?*

115. Which of these is not a type of ship: **frigate, destroyer, cruiser, fighter, tanker, trawler**

116. How can you see
through walls?

117. How many squares are there in this diagram?

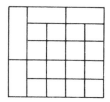

118. A frog tries to crawl out of a well 30m deep. He
climbs 3m every hour but slips back 2m. How
long will it take him to climb out of the well?

119. Can you find the six-letter word made up of the
two three-letter words found from these clues: a
form of transport — to go bad?

120. What do these numbers all have in common: **18,
12, 60, 48, 30, 6, 78**

121. Use your tangram pieces to make this shape:

122. Who provides you with **REPRINTS**?

123. If A can run a mile in 4.12 minutes and B can run 4.12 miles in an hour, which is the faster runner of the two?

124. Can you corect the two mistakes in this sentence?

125. What is hot about the letter B?

126. One word from each of these sequences has got into the wrong sequence. Which words are they: **day, month, week, tyre, minute — battery, starter, gear, second, wiper**?

127. Study the figure below and count how many triangles you can see.

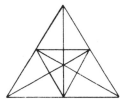

128. What do you get if you add 1 to 19 six times?

129. Can you rearrange the words in this jumbled sentence to produce the right answer: *Nine times three will not divided, but three divided by eight go by three goes.*

130. Can you think of a six-letter word with the same meaning as 'threaten' which is made from the two three-letter words given by these clues: The opposite of women — top card in the pack.

131. Use your tangram pieces to make this shape:

132. What was the name of the girl who went **RIDING**?

133. What is the next number in this sequence: 9 1 2 8 3 4 ...?

134. What is the first high number that ends with a member of the cat family?

135. Which five-letter word has 6 left when you subtract 2 letters?

136. Which of these is the odd one out: **Burmese, Pekinese, Siamese, Maltese, Chinese, Japanese**

137. Move one match from this pattern to correct the equation:

138. What is the difference between six dozen dozen and a half dozen dozen?

139. Can you think of a six-letter word made from the two three-letter words given in these clues, both of which have similar meanings: a small creature — a household animal. Both words begin with P.

140. What do these all have in common: **main, mast, made, mate, matt, mace?**

141. Use your tangram pieces to make this shape:

142. Who enjoys **EASTER** most after fasting in Lent?

143. How can you take 1 from 19 and leave 20?

144. Which letter do you need to add to the beginning and end of this word to make a country: ... **ATIO** ...?

145. Which letter in the alphabet stands for the ocean?

146. Which of these is not a make of road vehicle: **Honda, Ford, BL, Boeing, Toyota, Chrysler?**

147. Take a piece of paper 15cm long and 3cm wide. Now try and cut this into five parts so that it can be rearranged to form a square.

148. How many times does the minute hand of a clock pass the hour hand between twelve noon and twelve midnight?

149. Can you correct this sentence: *Unrefined owl is called rude ale*?

150. Inside this word is another word with a similar meaning. Can you discover what it is: **SALVAGE**?

151. Use your tangram pieces to make this shape:

152. In which South Sea country would you dance the **TANGO**?

153. What is the next number in this sequence: **3 12 60 360 . . .**?

154. The last syllable of the first word is also the first syllable of the second word. Can you fill in the missing syllable: **All . . . ing**

155. Which animal is taller sitting down than standing up?

156. One of the words from this first group has got mixed with the second group. Which is it: **honey, jam, butter, marmite — bacon, sausages, marmalade, mushrooms.**

157. Take three matches from this pattern and leave three squares:

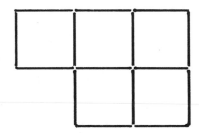

158. If there are eight notes to an octave on a piano keyboard and fifteen notes to two octaves, how many notes are there to three octaves?

159. What is the next number in this sequence: **31 28 31 30 31 . . .?**

358

160. Can you think of a measure used in cooking which begins with a piece of kitchen furniture and ends with a piece of cutlery?

161. Use your tangram pieces to construct this shape:

162. What is the difference between a rising and a setting sun?

163. A farmer owns a group of sheep and turkeys that together have a total of 99 heads and feet. How many are there of each type of animal if there are twice as many turkeys as sheep?

164. Study this pattern of dots and decide how many rows there are each containing 3 dots:

165. What is the multi-coloured word that has a first half connected with road building and a second half connected with the sun?

166. Where on a ship would you look for cards?

167. One of these numbers is an odd one out. Which is it: 24, 48, 16, 30, 96, 32, 40?

168. There is a three-letter word which placed in front of all of these half-finished words will complete them. What is the missing word: **TED, DON, ADE, ENT, ROT**?

169. Can you correct this sentence in which the words have got into the wrong order: *The First queen of England was Queen Elizabeth.*

170. What is the hidden word in **ILLUMINATED** that has the same meaning?

171. Use your tangram pieces to make this shape:

172. What colour are these unusual **CLARETS**?

173. What is the next number in this sequence:
1 10 18 25 31 36. . . .?

174. Fill in the missing letters to find the name of a famous film star: **xOxN xRxVxLxA**

175. Where do golfers dance?

176. One of these is an odd one out. Which is it: **George, Alfred, James, Simon, Charles, William, Edward**

177. Which is the longer of these two horizontal lines?

178. Which letter would you need to add to a shortened form of **ANTHONY** to get a word meaning rocky?

179. Can you correct this sentence: *Danny's ant and uncle hive on a farm wear they rare pigs and hens because the land is not futile.*

180. What do all of these have in common: **badger, owl, nightingale, bat**

181. Use your tangram pieces to make this pattern:

182. What do you have to pass through in this question to get to the **STAGE**?

183. If you had to put numbers on 100 lockers starting with 1 and ending with 100, how many 9's would you need?

184. How can you get a six-lettered ancient story from a three-lettered part of your body and the finish of everything?

185. What is black and white and red all over?

186. Which of these is not a tree: **oak, elm, ash, willow, bamboo, teak, chestnut.**

187. Move two of the matches in this pattern to leave nothing:

188. Two delicious treats are jumbled here. One is an expensive drink, the other a popular seasonal dish. Cross out pairs or groups of letters to find one and expose the other: **CH, TU, AM, PA, RK, GNE, EY**

189. Use your tangram pieces to construct this shape:

190. There is something wrong with this sentence. Can you correct it: *Charles I walked and talked half-an-hour after his head was cut off?*

191. What do you get when you add a baby's bed to a heavy weight and produce a common material used for clothing?

192. What can you suffer from if you travel on crowded **TRAINS**?

193. What do these numbers have in common: 2 3 5 9 17 33

194. Fill in the missing letters to find the name of this famous story: **xNxW xHxTx AxD xHx SxVxN xWxRxS**

195. Why were the elephants the last to leave Noah's ark?

196. One of each of these groups of words has got lost in the wrong group. Can you identify which they are: **port, harbour, dock, platform, quay — signal-box, ticket-office, line, points, jetty.**

197. Can you divide this equilateral triangle into four equal-sized pieces?

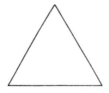

198. Imagine that a friend (call him Joe) tells you, '*I am going to a party. It's my uncle's only brother's son's party.*' Whose party is he going to?

199. From which number between 1 and 9 can you take away half and leave nothing?

200. How can you get one of the planets by adding sitting in the past to a three-letter word that sounds the same as making money?

201. Use your tangram pieces to make this shape:

202. What should you use when you want to **REDUST**?

203. If my 2 hens lay 2 eggs in 2 days, how many eggs will 6 hens lay in 6 days?

204. What is the word hidden in **FEASTING** that has the same meaning?

205. What do ducks and icicles have in common?

206. Which of these is not an ocean: **Pacific, Arctic, Atlantic, Indian, Mediterranean?**

207. See if you can rearrange these dots so that they form three straight lines each with an odd number of dots:

208. What makes coins marked Charles I very rare?

209. Start with a number, double it, redouble, divide by three and then by two. The answer is four. What number did you start with?

210. How can you combine a gentle tap (study this word carefully) with a four-letter, noisy, uncontrolled crowd attack to produce a person who loves his or her country?

211. Use your tangram pieces to construct this pattern:

212. What are **SAMEN** and **MENSA**?

213. If a fourth of forty were six, what would be a third of twenty?

214. Can you think of a four-letter word which added to these half-completed words will form full words:
... port, ... ion, com ..., ... age, ... enger?

215. Big as a biscuit, deep as a cup, even a river cannot fill it up. What do you think it is (remember the water pouring through it)?

216. Which of these is the odd one out: ., ;, ?, ', +, !, :?

217. Can you take four matches from this pattern and alter the position of three others to get 'O' as scored in ball games?

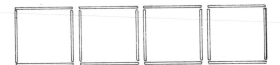

218. Is it ever likely that New Year's Eve and New Year's Day have fallen in the same year?

219. What is the four-letter word hidden in DEVILISH which has the same meaning?

220. Can you correct
this sentence
which has become
jumbled: **In Spain
the plain falls rain
on the mainly?**

221. Use your tangram pieces to
construct this shape:

222. If a chief no longer **REIGNS**, what does he do?

223. If three cats can catch three mice in three
minutes, how many cats are needed to catch
one hundred mice in one hundred minutes?

224. Fill in the missing letters to identify this film:
xHx ExPxRx SxRxKxS xAxK

225. Where was King Solomon's temple?

226. Which of these is not a nut: **cashew, peanut,
coconut, Brazil, hazel, walnut, banana, monkey?**

227. If two matches laid as an X = No, can you move one match to produce Yes. (You can bend a match if you want to)

228. The names of two famous commanders are mixed here. Can you identify who is who: **Horatio Arthur Wellesley Nelson Wellington?**

229. How many times can you subtract 22 from 2,222?

230. Which four-letter word meaning comfort has to be added to these groups of letters to produce words meaning stop and to make someone happy: **c ... — pl ...?**

231. Use your tangram pieces to construct this shape:

232. Where do tough chickens come from?

233. What is the next number in this sequence: 4 4
16 5 5 25 6 6 36 . . .?

234. How can you put a boy between **BAL** and **DER**
to make two six-letter words?

235. Which public building is the highest?

236. Can you spot the odd one out in this sequence:
**Thames, Severn, Avon, Clyde, Ouse, Tyne,
Trent?**

237. Study this pattern of dots. Then work out how
many rows there are containing four dots.

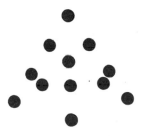

238. Can you think of an animal that first walks on
four legs, then on two and in old age three?

239. The middle letter of this word is G. There are
three letters on either side, and the word refers
to a place where you buy drinks and a way of
getting things. What is the word?

240. These all have one thing in common; what is it: **lawn, hedge, hair, nails, hay, wheat?**

241. Use your tangram pieces to make this shape:

242. Which type of beer do some beer-drinkers call **REGAL?**

243. When do 1 and 1 make more than 2?

244. Fill in the missing letters to find the name of this tennis player: **xIxGxNxA xAxE**

245. What do we always leave behind because they are dirty?

246. Can you work out the meaning of this curious sentence: **Y Y U R Y Y U B I C U R Y Y for me.**

247. One member from each of these two groups is lost in the other group. Which are the lost words: **dinghy, yacht, windsurfer, kayak, kite** — **punt, canoe, rowing-boat, skiff, balloon**?

248. Move one match in this pattern and make a square:

249. Now see if you can correct the mistakes in this sentence: *The hart is an organ which pumps blood throw the artilleries.*

250. Which word connected with moving through the water would you find at the end of two words describing a digging action and sadness?

251. Use your tangram pieces to construct this shape:

252. What are the next two numbers in the sequence: **3 6 12 24 . . .**?

253. What is it that the spy
ERECTS?

254. Fill in the missing letters
to find the name of this
famous place in London:
xRxFxLxAx SxUxRx

255. What can you add to a
bucket of water to make it
weigh less?

256. Which of these is not a precious stone:
**diamond, ruby, emerald, quartz, sapphire,
pearl**?

257. How many triangles are
there in this figure?

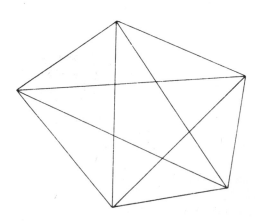

258. If five men take five days to mow five fields, how many days will it take one man to mow one field?

259. How can you add a form of cereal to a plate to get a holding action of eight letters?

260. Can you make a word connected with tiredness from: **4 E's, 2 L's, 1 N, 1 P, and 5 S's?**

261. Use your tangram pieces to make this pattern:

262. What sort of pliers does the mathematician use?

263. What number do you need to bring a lady who faints?

264. What do you get when you add the bottom of a dress to an insect and why would a choir be interested in it?

265. Which word allows you to take away two letters and get one?

266. One of these words is an odd one out; which is it: **Beech, sand, gravel, pebbles, shingle**?

267. Which of these three horizontal lines is the longest:

268. How much earth is there in a hole that measures one metre wide, by two metres long, by one-and-a-half metres deep?

269. How can you add a three-lettered form of head-gear to a four-lettered measurement and end up with a means of upsetting a boat?

270. What do the following all have in common: **dollar, dime, nickel, buck, cent**?

271. Use your tangram pieces to make this shape:

272. Who was the girl who was frightened of the **ALIENS**?

273. Can you think of a four-figure number in which the first digit is half the last the digit, the second digit is three less than the third digit, and the third digit multiplied by 2 equals the sum of the first and last digit?

274. Can you find the three-letter word which ends **VIO** . . . and begins . . . **TER**?

275. Who settled in the West before anyone else?

276. Which of these is the odd one out: **field, pasture, meadow, pond, prairie**?

277. Move four matches in this pattern and make 10 squares:

278. Can you translate this well-known proverb:
LETTER RATE THAN FEVER?

279. Two famous names are combined here; whose
are they? **Queen of Wales the Princess Mother
Elizabeth Queen the**

280. Another word for **FETCH** is hidden in this
word. What is it: **TOGETHER?**

281. Use your tangram pieces to
construct this shape:

282. What sort of person enjoys going for a
RAMBLE?

283. Study this progression and
work out the next number
to the right of the last
equals sign:

$$1 \times 9 - 1 = 8$$
$$21 \times 9 - 1 = 188$$
$$321 \times 9 - 1 = 2888$$
$$4321 \times 9 - 1 = ?$$

284. Which letter must you add to ... **OIN** ... at both the beginning and end to get anywhere?

285. Which fruit has been known for as long as men have used calendars?

286. Which of these has nothing to do with music: **violin, piano, harp, vacuum-cleaner, drum, flute?**

287. If you had to mend a hole in a floor that was two feet wide and twelve feet long and you were given a piece of wood three feet wide and eight feet long, how could you cut the board into two pieces so that they completely covered the hole but didn't overlap. Here is the shape of the hole (a) and the board (b):

288. What is in the middle of **SPAIN**?

289. There is something wrong about this statement. What is it: *The Sewage Canal is in Egypt?*

290. With just four letters you can make three words that have similar meanings to: the mail, finish and a place. What are the four letters and the three words?

291. Use your tangram pieces to make this pattern:

292. What sort of trousers did **ALFRED** use to wear?

293. Which is the next number in this series: **98 95 89 77 53** . . .?

294. Can you find a shelter in **ATTENTIVE**?

295. What can you hold without touching it?

296. Can you spot which of the words from the second group has found its way into the first group: **physics, history, chemistry, biology, maths — geography, music, art, literature**

297. How many pieces can you divide this circle into by drawing just three lines across it:

298. How many letters are there in the alphabet?

299. It's wrong to describe herrings swimming about the sea in 'shawls', but it's only just wrong. What should you say?

300. Here's a country you may not immediately recognize, but by rearranging the letters you'll easily discover it. What's its real name: **DENWALNEAZ**

301. Use your tangram pieces to form this shape:

302. What sort of fruit comes from the **ARGENTINE**?

303. What does this number equal $99\frac{99}{99}$?

304. Fill in the missing letters to find the name of this famous actor: .xAxRxNxE xLxVxEx

305. How was the blind carpenter able to see?

306. Which of these has nothing to do with flying: **wing, cockpit, basket, glider, windsurfer, hang-glider**?

307. Take eight matches from this pattern and leave four squares:

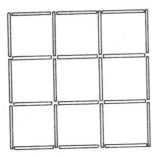

308. Why did the chicken cross the road?

309. Can you think of three letters that arranged in different ways will give you words that mean: **possess, at the moment** and **gained victory?**

310. What do the following have in common: **shoe, boot, saddle, belt, wallet, jacket, whip, chair?**

311. Use your tangram pieces to make this pattern:

312. On which island would you look for **DIARIANS?**

313. What will be the next two numbers in this sequence: 1 4 2 8 4 16 ...?

314. What letter do you need to add to the beginning and end of ... NGIN ... to get a source of power?

315. Which kind of nut doesn't have a shell?

316. One of the entries in the first group has accidentally been printed in the second group. Do you know which it is: **French, Spanish, German, Latin, Greek —** **Chinese, Arabic, Hindi, Urdu, Persian?**

317. Study this diagram and then try and go over each line once without lifting your pencil off the page or crossing a line you have already drawn.

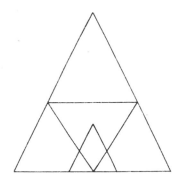

318. Which word do English speakers from Quebec always pronounce wrongly?

319. What is wrong with this sentence: *An executive is a man who chops off people's heads?*

320. What is the other word for lazy hidden in the word **INDOLENT** which has a similar meaning too?

321. Use your tangram pieces to construct this shape:

322. Who **ENTERS** this question?

323. Can you do the seemingly impossible and think of two whole numbers that multiplied together will produce 7?

324. Fill in the missing letters to discover the identity of this detective: **xHxRxOxK xOxMxS**

325. When do you travel as fast as a sports car?

326. Which of these is the odd one out: **carpet, mat, rug, linoleum, curtain, tile**?

327. See if you can arrange 10 dots in five rows each containing 4 dots.

328. What do you always try to keep because nobody else wants it?

329. What is wrong with this statement: *I watched a metaphor shower in the sky last night?*

330. Add a girl's name of four-letters to **PRI** to come first.

331. Use your tangram pieces to construct this pattern:

332. Which girl is unfairly called **INANE?**

333. Look at this sequence of numbers and then circle every combination of three successive numbers that adds up to 15:

7 1 4 2 1 2 8 3 5 4 2 4 9 5 6 6 3 7

334. Which three-letter word must you add to the end of **NIT** . . . and the beginning of . . . **HER** in order to make two six-letter words?

335. What has six legs but only walks on four?

336. Which of the words from the first group is hidden in the second group: **surgeon, nurse, ward, X-ray** — **restaurant, manager, casualty, bar, ball-room**?

337. Study this shape and then move four matches to leave three equilateral triangles:

338. Here is a clue to the four-word answer with this number of letters in each word (4, 6, 3, 4): Don't jump to conclusions? What's the answer?

339. What do all of these have in common: **commander, captain, admiral, petty-officer, rating, lieutenant**?

340. Which country is this **NEDEWS**?

341. Use your tangram pieces to construct this pattern:

342. What did Neil **ARMSTRONG** need when he climbed down the ladder on to the moon for the first time?

343. What will be the next number in this sequence: 2 1 1 3 1 1?

344. Which letter do you need to add to **WIS** to get a European nationality?

345. When do you step in poodles?

346. Which of these is the odd one out: **wheat, barley, raisins, oats, rye?**

347. Move three matches in this pattern to form four equal squares:

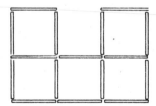

348. What happens at Christmas time?

349. What must you do to this sentence to correct it: *The Pope lives in the Vacuum?*

350. She was named after a city in Italy and a bird connected with the evening. What was her name?

351. Use your tangram pieces to construct this pattern:

352. Which nationality, in this question at least, is **BIANGULAR**?

353. How can six 1's be made to add up to 12 using only one plus sign?

354. Fill in the missing letters to find something to eat: **xAxAxOxI xHxExE**.

355. What colour is rain?

356. Which of these would you not find living in a zoo: **elephant, dodo, zebra, lion, tiger, hyena**?

357. Look at this pattern and then add two more dots to form ten rows each containing three dots:

358. What did the highwayman say (5, 3, 7)?

359. The words in this sentence have become jumbled. Can you put them back into their correct order: *The red car and light stop not did the drove through*?

360. Which three-letter word added to each of these will form four complete words: **TOON, CASE, AWAY, BONS**?

361. Use your tangram pieces to construct this pattern:

362. Which royal family lives in **STROUD**?

363. Which is the next number in this sequence: 2 17 37 62 92 . . .?

364. Can you think of a well-known dance from which you can take a 'tin' and still be left with a 'tin'?

365. What has a neck but no head?

366. Find the member of the first group that has got into the second group and the member of the second group that is in the first: **chocolate, sherbert, licorice, vinegar** — **lemon, lime, yogurt, honey.**

367. Look at the times shown on these digital clocks and work out the time shown on the next one: 2-10 3-20 4-40 6- . . .?

368. Which month of the year is the parade sergeant always shouting?

369. What is wrong with this statement: *The mare war his chane of offence?*

370. Which country on earth can you find in most kitchens?

371. Use your tangram pieces to construct this pattern:

372. What did Dick **TURPIN** eat before he rode to York?

373. Look at this sequence of numbers and then circle the combinations of three successive numbers that add up to 15: 9 3 1 8 3 4 0 7 8 5 6 5 5 5 2 4 8 6

374. How can you add the chief (minus a letter) to a heavy weight to make an American city with six letters?

375. What can you put in a glass but never remove from it?

376. Which of these is the odd one out: **rubber, cork, plywood, aluminium, olive oil**?

377. What do you think the missing numbers should be in this sum:

$$\begin{array}{r} ??? \\ + \ 675 \\ \hline 918 \end{array}$$

378. Which months with 31 days adjoin each other in the year?

379. Can you correct the mistakes in this sentence: *The peeple who live in Paris are called Parasites?*

380. Who is hiding in this sentence: *Everyone said the man was daring in the super way he came to help?*

381. Use your tangram pieces to construct this pattern:

382. Which Indian language does this **BELGIAN** speak?

383. Which three figures multiplied by 5 will make 6?

384. What did one kennel-man say to the other at feeding time (2, 2, 3, 4)?

385. What happens to horses when they grow old?

386. Which of these is not a royal home: **Windsor, Sandringham, Balmoral, Blenheim, Highgrove, Gatcombe?**

387. Cut three pieces of card shaped like (a) and one piece each of (b) and (c) and see if you can fit them together to form a cross.

a.　　　　　b.　　　　　c.

388. Where did the shot go (2, 3, 3)?

389. *My Dad sings base in the choir* — what's wrong with this statement?

390. Three letters form part of the head, a period of time and the plural of '**is**'. What are the letters and the words formed from them?

391. What was the word for '**yes**' when everyone wore **LIVERY?**

392. What will be the next two numbers in this sequence: 8 4 7 3 6 2 . . .?

393. Use your tangram pieces
to construct this shape:

394. Which vegetable must
you add before and after
'O' to make a small bang?

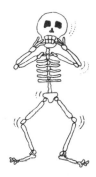

395. Why are skeletons cowards?

396. Which of these is the odd one out: **plastic,
polythene, plaster, petrol**?

397. Where do rockets fly (3, 4)?

398. What did the writer of this sentence mean:
*People who test your eyesight are called
optimists*?

399. Which country is this: **ANADAC**?

400. Look at this pattern and work out how many rows there are each containing 4 dots:

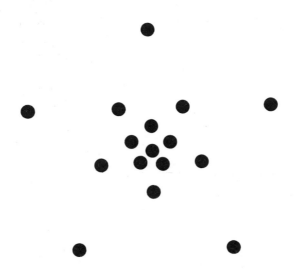

401. Use your tangram pieces to construct this pattern:

402. What does the
DEALER do again
in a card game?

403. What is the number which will give you 4 after
you have added 8, subtracted 8, multiplied what
is left by 8 and finally divided the result by
twice 4?

404. Fill in the missing letters to find this car: **xOxD
xIxRxA**

405. What goes up and never comes down?

406. Sort out the odd one in this group: **Alps, Andes,
Himalayas, Antarctica, Atlas**

407. Take away one match
and move four others
in this pattern to
make 11 squares:

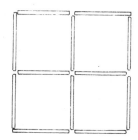

408. Who is the aircrew-man who also steers a ship into port?

409. Reorder this sentence to correct it: *Alfred the burned not the Great cakes Arthur.*

410. What is the link between these: **fear, care, earring, reap, declare**?

411. Use your tangram pieces to construct this pattern:

412. What did the **CORKER** do to the half-finished bottle?

413. Look at this sequence of numbers and then circle every three consecutive ones that add up to 15: **2 3 4 5 6 7 6 5 4 3 2 4 6 7 8 3 6 2**

414. How can you add a popular drink to a way of spoiling something and . . . **GER** to produce two six-letter words?

415. When does eleven plus two equal one?

416. Which is the odd one out in this sequence: **house, bungalow, hutch, warren, apartment, flat, mansion?**

417. Which of these two oblongs is the taller?

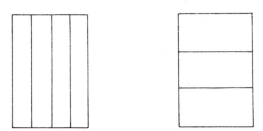

418. How can you join two pieces of wood by hand?

419. Can you correct this statement: *Reefs are put on coffins?*

420. Which Europeans are hidden in **SPANNED?**

421. Use your tangram pieces to construct this pattern:

422. What sort of ant is good at counting?

423. If you remember previous questions you might know how to make six 9's equal 100. If you've forgotten, can you work it out anyhow?

424. Which letter must you add to ... **UTTO** ... followed by the letter that follows it to produce something you'd find in a butcher's shop?

425. What is the difference between here and there?

426. One of these is in the wrong group; which is it: **kidney, lung, brain, liver, skin, blood.**

427. Look at this pattern and then add three more dots to form eight rows of three dots:

428. Which Scottish poet had trouble with fire?

429. Liquids come in litres not puppies. What do they come in?

430. What sound can you find in **ASCENSION**?

431. Use your tangram pieces to construct this pattern:

432. What ancient marks fetch high prices at **SALES**?

433. Which are the next two numbers in this sequence: **37 30 29 22 21 14 . . .?**

434. Add a drink to the beginning and end of **ABLE** to get a type of medicine.

435. What do people make that we can't see?

436. Spot the odd one out in this group: **grizzly, polar, koala, brown, black, teddy, leopard.**

437. How many different squares are there in this figure and how many triangles?

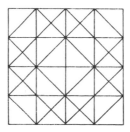

438. What illness is this spelt in this unusual way: **NEWMOANYHERE?**

439. *Kings wear robes made with the fur of vermin.* True or false?

440. Which part of an aircraft do you find in its **AIRCREWS?**

441. Use your tangram pieces to construct this pattern:

442. Which actress always gives a **STARTLE?**

443. Can you fill in the missing numbers in this sequence:

$$15873 \times 7 = 111111$$
$$15873 \times 14 = 222222$$
$$15873 \times ? = 333333$$
$$15??? \times 28 = ?????4$$

444. Which three letters will turn **KIP** . . . into a food and . . . **MIT** into a licence?

445. Why should you never
believe a person in bed?

446. Which of the words from the first group has got
into the second group: **stone, rock, boulder,
chip** — **concrete, cement, mortar, pebble**

447. Move one match in this equation to produce the
correct answer:

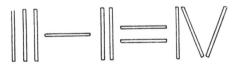

448. What happened to the bowler who had the
maximum number of runs scored of one ball (2,
3, 3, 3, 3)

449. Why is this statement wrong: *The masculine of
vixen is vicar?*

450. Which nation is good at bringing a shine to furniture?

451. Use your tangram pieces to construct this pattern:

452. Who brought about the downfall of **SAMSON**? (The answer lies in the stones)

453. Which is the next number in this sequence: **99 91 75 51 . . .?**

454. Which letter must you add to the beginning and end of . . . **EGA** . . . to make it agree with the law?

455. Why is mayonnaise never ready?

456. Spot the odd one out in this series: **in, on, at, over, below, behind, before, after, even, beside.**

457. Which three-letter tipping of the head gives a shortened boy's name backwards?

458. Look at this magic square. All the rows, columns and diagonals add up to the same number. Can you fill in the missing numbers?

17	24	1	8	15
?	5	7	14	16
4	?	13	20	22
10	12	19	?	3
11	18	25	2	?

459. What's wrong with this sentence: *When we was top we was goodest in the class?*

460. What part of the plumbing system can you find in **ENGRAINED?**

461. Use your tangram pieces to construct this pattern:

462. Who lives in **ANTRIM?**

463. What are the next two numbers in this sequence: 1 4 9 16 25 36 . . .?

464. Fill in the missing letters to find this American landmark: **xTxTxE xF xIxExTx**

465. What can you serve but never eat?

466. One of these is out of place; which is it: **telephone, television, telegraph, telescope, telegram**?

467. Move one match in this equation to get the right result:

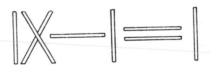

468. What goes on a finger and sounds a bell?

469. Can you unscramble this sentence: *The minutes was running late train fifteen.*

470. Add a boy's name to . . . **BED** to get floated.

471. Use your tangram pieces
to construct this shape:

472. What does the **SADDLER** climb up?

473. What are the next two numbers in this
sequence: **1 7 2 7 3 7** . . . ?

474. Which pet can you find in **NOTECASE**?

475. What has cities without houses, rivers with no
water and woods without trees?

476. Which is the odd one out in this group: **fez,
helmet, turban, cap, sandal, beret**?

477. Which of these four figures is the tallest:

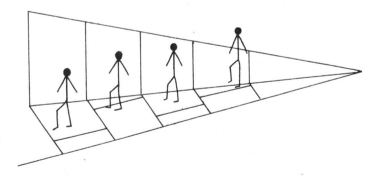

478. Can you complete the name: **Charles (waterproof coat)**?

479. Can you correct this sentence: *A fjord is a type of Norwegian car*?

480. Which is this country: **ASIURS**?

481. Use your tangram pieces to construct this pattern:

482. Which river suffers from **NERVES**?

483. How can you add 54 to . . . **ING** to produce being alive?

484. Fill in the missing letters to find this sports site: **xOxTxAxL xTxDxUx**

485. When do clocks die?

486. Which of these is the odd one out: **rickshaw, tandem, wheel-barrow, trolley**?

487. Take six matches and use them to form three-and-a-half-dozen.

488. What would you be if you jumped off the Eiffel Tower? (2, 5)

489. Can you correct this sentence: *A pemmican is a large bird with a large bill?*

490. Can you add a man's name to a cricket hat to make part of a ship's equipment?

491. Use your tangram pieces to form this pattern:

492. Which chief enjoys **HIKES**?

493. Look at this row of numbers and circle every three consecutive numbers that add up to 15: 1 4 9 1 6 8 8 2 5 3 6 4 9 6 4 8 1 1

494. Fill in the missing letters to find this novelist: **xHxRxEx DxCxExS**

495. What can you always count on even when things go wrong?

496. Which of these has nothing to do with water:
rain, marine, brine, lagoon, marshal, stream?

497. See if you can fill in the missing numbers in this
sum:

$$\begin{array}{r} ??5 \\ +\ 74? \\ \hline 96? \end{array}$$

498. Add an earl's name to complete this snack:
CHEESE . . .?

499. What is wrong with this sentence: *Protecting
the countryside is called conversation.*

500. Can you find a way to cure hidden in **LASHES**?

501. Use your tangram pieces
to make this pattern:

502. What do you find **INSIDE** a map of the East?

503. What will be the next number in this sequence:
91 28 73 46 . . .?

504. Which two letters must you add to the beginning and end of ... I ... to make you cry?

505. What increases in value when it is turned upside down?

506. Which of these is the odd one out: **encyclopedia, dictionary, thesaurus, almanac, novel?**

507. Trace this triangle and then decide the easiest way to divide it in half:

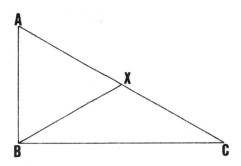

508. Who spend Sunday mornings pulling ropes? (4, 7)

509. Can you correct this sentence: *Sodium Sulphate is another name for the Shah of Iran?*

510. What do the following have in common: **A, E, I, O, U, W, Y?**

511. Use your tangram pieces to construct this pattern:

512. What does the **JAILER** do to the hardened criminal?

513. How quickly can you work out this sum? (If you're really sharp you'll do it without even using a pencil and paper)

$$50 + \frac{38}{76} + 49\frac{1}{2} = ?$$

514. Fill in the missing letters to find the name of this capital city: **xUxNxS xIxEx**

515. Why is it easy to weigh fish?

516. Which of these is the odd one out: **Chester, Oxford, Bedford, Warwick, Buckingham, Berkshire?**

517. Take six matches and arrange them so that each one touches the other five.

518. Add a famous general to a type of footwear to go for a walk in the rain.

519. Can you correct this sentence: *Soviet is another name for table napkin*?

520. Which large Asian country can you find in **INDICATOR**?

521. Use your tangram pieces to construct this pattern:

522. What must you do with the **POSTER** sent to the wrong address?

523. How can you make 5 odd numbers add together to make 14?

524. Which letter goes before and after ... **RE** ... to get a portion of land?

525. What is in fashion but always out of date?

526. Which of these is the odd one out: **shampoo, soap, toothpaste, detergent, shaving cream**?

527. What important sporting event was celebrated at the Knotted Mug? (3, 3)

528. Which of the lines in this diagram is longer, AB or AC?

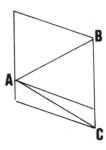

529. What is wrong with this sentence: *People living on the equator are called equestrians*?

530. How can you find a word for stacking in **SPLIT-RING**?

531. Use your tangram pieces to construct this shape:

532. Who lives in **ARMAGH**?

533. What is the next number in this sequence: 27 9 11 8 9 10 9 . . .?

534. How can you get a journey out of **OUTRIGHT**?

535. For which man do all other men take off their hats?

536. Which of these is the odd one out: **kangaroo, horse, dog, pig, cow, rabbit**?

537. Look at this magic square and then fill in the missing numbers. All the rows, columns and diagonals add up to the same number:

16	3	?	13
5	10	11	8
?	6	7	12
4	15	14	?

538. Why is the letter A like noon?

539. Can you correct this jumbled sentence: *I like when rains but not holiday it on going*?

540. What do the following all have in common: **Alsatian, Labrador, Great Dane, Golden Retriever**?

541. Use your tangram pieces to construct this pattern:

542. What sort of snow cuts through you like **STEEL**?

543. Can you work out this fraction without even doing a sum:

$$81 \, \frac{5643}{297}$$

544. Fill in the missing letters to find this tree:
xOxPxR xExCx

545. When is a black dog not a black dog?

546. Which is the odd one out in this group: **John, James, Paul, George, Ringo**?

547. Move two matches from this pattern to make 11 squares:

548. How can you frighten a dairy product by adding S?

549. What is wrong with this sentence: *Five times three is the same as sixty divided by 3?*

550. Which sea animal lives in **CHELSEA**?

551. Use your tangram pieces to construct this pattern:

552. Which mechanical tool provides the most **CHATTER**?

553. Look at this row of numbers and then circle every set of three consecutive numbers that add up to 15: 1 9 1 4 8 3 2 9 4 5 3 8 6 7 4 9 2 1

554. Which two letters (that follow each other in the alphabet) must you add to ... **ANAN** ... to make a fruit?

555. Which is the best way to win a race?

556. Which of these is the odd one out: **Liverpool Street, Paddington, Victoria, Oxford Circus, Waterloo**?

557. What is wrong with this sentence: *A Scotland Yard is shorter than an English yard?*

558. Study these two diagrams. In which of them are the horizontal lines parallel?

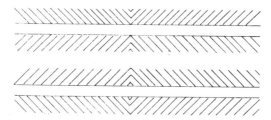

559. His name almost sounds like a plant that grows in damp places and he invented a famous way of communicating with only two symbols. What was his name?

560. Which country is this: **MEANY GEARST**

561. Use your tangram pieces to construct this pattern:

562. What is the next number in this sequence: **2 6 16 25 36 49 . . . ?**

563. Who owns a very **SAILABLE** boat?

564. Fill in the missing letters to discover who this is: **xHx MxN xN xHx MxOx**

565. What has everyone else had that Adam and Eve didn't have?

566. Which of these is the odd one out: **church, cathedral, abbey, mosque, college, chapel**?

567. Look at this magic square in which the numbers in every row, column and diagonal add up to the same number and then fill in the missing numbers:

$$
\begin{array}{ccc}
2 & 9 & ? \\
7 & 5 & 3 \\
6 & ? & 8
\end{array}
$$

568. What is wrong with this sentence: *The French for Mr is Monsoon?*

569. His name begins and ends with a smell but he invented an important means of writing. Who was he in four letters?

570. Which country is this: **SAPKINTA**

571. Use your tangram pieces to construct this pattern:

572. What does the pop star spend his time doing when he is not **SIGNING** autographs?

573. What are the next two numbers in this
sequence: 8 6 4 2 7 5 . . .?

574. How can you add as well to . . . K, . . . L, . . . TH
to make three complete words?

575. Can you spell a composition in only two letters?

576. Which of these is the odd man out: **net, racket,
ball, stump, linesman**?

577. Take a pile of 11 coins or counters. Take five
from these. How can you add four, and have
nine left?

578. What unit of electricity is named after him?
(The answer is in the question if you look
closely)

579. What is wrong with this sentence: *an oxygen is
a figure with eight sides*?

580. How can you find tidy
in **GREATNESS**?

581. Use your tangram pieces
to construct this pattern:

582. Which books in the book
shop are the **UNDEAR**
ones?

583. What is the next number in this sequence:
212 323 454 565 656 ...?

584. What four-letter vehicle should you add to ... **P**
to walk?

585. What is ploughed but never planted?

586. Which is the odd one out in this sequence:
Sahara, Gibson, Gobi, Greenland, Ghana?

587. Using this odd shaped piece of wood how could
you make a table-top two feet square in just
two sawings?

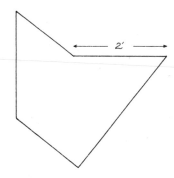

588. Which cricketer has a hat named after him?

589. What is wrong with this sentence: *A mummy is
a gypsy's dead mother*?

590. Add a three-letter girl's name to an afternoon meal to produce a four-letter fat used in cooking.

591. Use your tangram pieces to construct this pattern:

592. How are **TWEEDS** best cooked?

593. If **33** × **3367** = **111111** and **66** × **3367** = **222222**, what will **132** × **3367 equal** (without working out the sum)?

594. Which three letters give you a rodent, a material used to make a road and something seen in a gallery?

595. Why did the old man put wheels on his wheelchair?

596. Which of these is the odd one out: **Salmon, eel, cod, trout, herring, plaice?**

597. Move two of the matches in this equation to
make it read correctly:

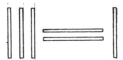

598. Who stands and has stood higher than most of
us above London and yet sees only half what we
can see?

599. What is wrong with this sentence: *Lady Godiva
was the first woman to swim the English
Channel.*

600. Which boy's name should you add to ... **PLE**
to get a specimen?

601. Use your tangram pieces to construct this
pattern:

602. What do they build in **NAPLES**?

603. What are the next two numbers in this sequence: **1 12 3 11 5 10**

604. Fill in the missing letters to find this mighty construction: **xHx GxExT xAxL xF xHxNx**

605. How can you get two litres of milk into a one litre container?

606. Which of these is not a cathedral city: **Lincoln, Winchester, Durham, Salisbury, Reading, Exeter?**

607. Look at this magic square. The rows, columns and diagonals all add up to the same number. Can you fill in the missing numbers:

$$
\begin{array}{ccc}
6 & ? & 2 \\
1 & ? & 9 \\
8 & 3 & 4
\end{array}
$$

608. Why is the letter I like a broken leg in snow?

609. Can you unscramble this sentence: *England is not the river but in Europe the Thames in longest.*

610. What is genuine in **RELACE?**

611. Who uses a **GEIGER** counter?

612. How can you add 3 to 191 to produce a total which is less than 20?

613. Use your tangram pieces
to construct this pattern:

614. Fill in the missing letters to find this part of the
world: **xExTxAx AxExIxA**

615. What is too much for one, enough for two but
too much for three?

616. Which of these is the odd one out: **Saturn,
Neptune, Venus, Mars, Uranus, Sun, Jupiter**?

617. Each of the straight lines of numbers in this
magic star add up to the same total. Can you
fill in the missing numbers:

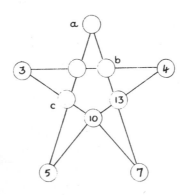

426

618. What do **Z** and **T** have in common?

619. What is wrong with this sentence: *The French national anthem is called the Mayonnaise?*

620. What do the following have in common: **rosemary, thyme, salt, pepper, garlic, mint?**

621. Use your tangram pieces to construct this pattern:

622. In which country does this **IGUANA** live?

623. How can you add 9 to **F** ... to mend something?

624. Which three letters give you a member of the monkey family and a garden vegetable?

625. Why is every bride unlucky on her wedding day?

626. Which of these is the odd one out: **Midland, Barclays. Lloyds, National Westminster, Boots?**

627. Take away two matches from this pattern of matches and leave two squares:

628. Find the proverb in this sentence: *Paint peart newer son pair lads.*

629. What is wrong with this sentence: *Manual Labour is a Spanish workman?*

630. How can you find pigs in **DWINDLES**?

631. Use your tangram pieces to construct this pattern:

632. Which is this **ANCESTRAL** city?

633. What are the next two numbers in this sequence: **8 4 7 3 6 2 ...?**

634. Which letter should you add to the beginning and end of ... **N CIRCL** ... to round it off?

635. Why did the timid man always take cold baths?

636. Which of these is the odd one out: **Bread, cake, roll, bun, pastry, cheese, biscuit**?

637. Which way is the barrel aligned; to the right or the left?

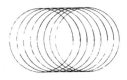

638. Why is H helpful to the deaf?

639. Can you correct this sentence: *In olden times even pheasants drank wine in France.*

640. Which country is hidden here: **COXIME**?

641. Use your tangram pieces to construct this pattern:

642. Who **LOWERS** the score in a two-man relay race?

643. Look at this sequence of numbers and then circle every three consecutive numbers that add up to 15: **5 9 4 8 3 7 4 8 5 9 8 7 6 5 4 3 2 1**

644. Fill in the missing letters to find this large family home: **xUxKxNxHxM xAxAxE**

645. Which coat has the most sleeves?

646. Which of these is the odd one out: **captain, major, colonel, general, brigadier, admiral, field marshall**

647. Look at this magic square in which the rows, columns and diagonals all add up to the same total and see if you can fill in the missing numbers:

1	14	15	?
8	11	10	5
12	?	6	9
13	2	?	16

648. Who gave his name to the seventh month of the year?

649. What is wrong with this sentence: *There is a country in South America called Equinox?*

650. How can you find part of your face in **INCHES**?

651. Use your tangram pieces to construct this shape:

652. Which Scotsman lives in **CREMONA**?

653. What is the next number in this sequence: **7 13 25 43 67 ...?** ·

654. Which letter goes at the beginning and end of ... **UNNE** ... to produce an athlete?

655. What sort of tea makes you feel secure?

656. Which of these is the odd one out: **Subaru, Datsun, Minolta, Honda, Toyota, Colt?**

657. How can you make this equation read correctly without touching a match?

658. He was a poet whose words were often thought to be worth more than those of any other poet. Who was he? (The answer is in the question 1.)

659. What is wrong with this sentence: *The man who discovered America was called Columbine*?

660. Which poet enjoyed **STEAKS**?

661. Use your tangram pieces to construct this pattern:

662. What piece of fishing equipment is hidden in **STRANGE**?

663. How can you make four 4's equal 64?

664. Fill in the missing letters to find this seat of learning: xNxVxRxIxY xF xAxIx

665. What sort of puzzle makes people angry?

666. Which of these has nothing to do with the weather: **wind, Sun, rain, frost, snow, Jupiter, hail**?

667. Look carefully at this sum. Is it really right? If not, how can you correct it without changing any of the figures?

$$
\begin{array}{r}
3u1u \\
3u0 \\
7u813 \\
\hline
u337u813
\end{array}
$$

668. What do you do when you turn your back on fiction? **(4, 3, 4)**

669. What is wrong with this definition: *autobiography is the story of motor cars*?

670. Which country is this: **MAZIBWEB**?

671. Use your tangram pieces to construct this pattern:

672. Which parts of bolts are the **HARDEST**

673. Look at this sequence of numbers and draw a circle round every three consecutive numbers that add up to 15: 2 4 8 1 6 3 2 6 4 1 2 8 2 5 6 1 2

674. Fill in the missing letters to find this tree: **xOxSx CxExTxUx**

675. How can you say rabbit without pronouncing the R?

676. Which of these is the odd one out: **canteen, restaurant, café, court, refectory, dining-room**?

677. Move one match in this equation to make it read correctly:

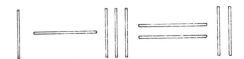

678. Which letter in the alphabet will give you a line of people?

679. What is wrong here: *A cartridge is a small game bird*?

680. What do all of these have in common: **cygnet, kitten, lamb, puppy, foal, calf**?

681. Use your tangram pieces to construct this pattern:

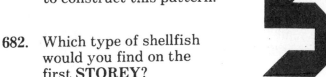

682. Which type of shellfish would you find on the first **STOREY**?

683. What is the next number in this sequence: 81 9 72 9 63 9 . . .?

684. Which type of three-letter sleep gives you a cooking implement?

685. What sort of animal is a nightmare?

686. Which of these is the odd one out: **Matthew, Mark, Luke, Paul, John?**

687. Which of these two circles is the larger (a) or (b)?

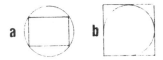

688. What is good about **T**?

689. What is wrong with this statement: *The earth resolves round the sun once every year?*

690. How can you find a wooden stake in **STOPPER?**

691. Use your tangram pieces to construct this pattern:

692. Can you fill in the missing numbers in this sum:

$$\begin{array}{r} ??4 \\ + \; ?82 \\ \hline 93? \end{array}$$

693. Why is a **SPEAR** useful to a farmer?

694. Fill in the missing letters to find this American landmark: **xHx NxAxAxA xAxLx?**

695. Who is paid to fall down on the job?

696. Which of these has nothing to do with the river: **lock, boat, bridge, weir, rapid, lay-by?**

697. Move two matches from this pattern to make four squares:

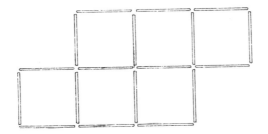

698. Which letter is the noisiest bird in the alphabet?

699. What is wrong with this sentence: *In the old days they used to write in hysterics*?

700. Which dead pop star still **LIVES** for many of his fans?

701. Use your tangram pieces to construct this pattern:

702. How can you find a horse in **LECTORS**?

703. Look at this sequence of numbers and then circle every group of three consecutive numbers that add up to 15: **2 4 8 1 6 3 2 6 4 1 2 8 2 5 6 5 1 2**

704. Which letter must you add to … **NTRANC** … to get into it?

705. What is always coming but never arrives?

706. Which of these is the odd one out: **Libra, Virgo, Leo, Scorpio, Pisces, Juno, Cancer, Aquarius**?

707. What follows B in the alphabet?

708. Make a copy of this shape and cut four of them the same size. Then see if you can fit them together to make the same shape but twice the size.

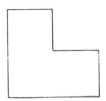

709. What is wrong with this statement: *Large birds that run but can't fly are called hostages?*

710. Which American president shares his name with a county in the eastern part of England?

711. Use your tangram pieces to construct this pattern:

712. What do you call a **RELATION** who lives in Hong Kong?

713. What is the next number in this sequence: **515 626 848 959 . . .?**

714. Fill in the missing letters to find this famous city: **xHx WxIxE xIxY**

715. What can you hold in your right hand but never in your left hand?

716. Which of these is the odd one out: **deck, hull, mast, funnel, bow, boot, stern, bridge**?

717. Move three matches in this pattern to leave three squares:

718. Which letter always asks a question?

719. What is wrong with this sentence: *I like to reed magasines*?

720. Which part of your body will you find in **EARTHILY**?

721. Use your tangram pieces to construct this pattern:

722. What sort of painting are **GOSLINGS** best at?

723. What is the next number in this sequence: **98 17 97 16 96 . . .?**

724. Fill in the missing letters to find this Wild West hero: **xUxFxLx BxLx**

725. What do all witches study at school?

726. Which of these is the odd one out: **fork, spade, knife, shovel, hoe, rake?**

727. Which of these angles is the larger (a) or (b)?

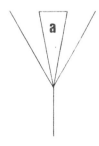

728. Why is O like a tidy room?

729. Can you correct this: *The liver is an infernal organ*?

730. What do the following have in common: **red, green, blue, white, yellow**?

731. Use your tangram pieces to construct this pattern:

732. Who lives in a **GEORGIAN** house?

733. Can you fill in the missing numbers in the second row:

8818	1111	8188	1881
8181	?	8811	?

734. Which letter should you add to the beginning and end of ... **ETHA** ... to make it deadly?

735. Which type of person is always fed up with people?

736. Which of these is the odd one out: **kettle, cooker, bunsen burner, fridge, sun-lamp**?

737. How many squares are there in this diagram?

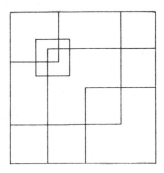

738. Which are the most explosive of all the letters in the alphabet?

739. What is wrong with this statement: *Water is made of hydrogin and nitrogin?*

740. What way can you find in **ORDAINS**?

741. Use your tangram pieces to form this shape:

742. Where in Canada should you go to hear an **ORATION?**

743. Can you fill in the missing numbers in this sequence:

$$1 \times 9 - 1 = 8$$
$$21 \times 9 - 1 = 188$$
$$?21 \times 9 - ? = ????$$

744. Which man must you divide in half before you can **HESITATE?**

745. What landed on this poor person's head and knocked them cold?

746. Which of these is the odd one out: **billiards, snooker, rugby, hockey, tennis, croquet?**

747. Move three matches in this pattern and end up with five triangles:

748. Why is D so important in marriage?

749. What is wrong with this: *a lightship is an empty cargo vessel?*

750. What do the following have in common: **watch, clock, sundial, chronometer, telephone, radio?**

751. Use your tangram pieces to construct this pattern:

752. Who has the best wood of **LARCHES?**

753. Without working it out on a calculator or a sheet of paper, what do you think think this sum equals:

$$\frac{148}{2.96} + \frac{35}{0.7} = ?$$

754. Fill in the missing letters to find this famous ocean feature near Australia: **xHx GxExT xAxRxEx RxEx**

755. How can you make seven even?

756. Which of these is the odd one out: **path, track, motorway, bridleway?**

757. Which letter is like death?

758. What is wrong with this sentence: *My father is retarded on a pension?*

759. Cut out nine pieces shaped like the one below and then use them to make a larger one which is the same shape but three times the size.

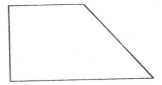

760. What do the following have in common: **bacon, ham, veal, chops, loin, brisket?**

761. Use your tangram pieces to make this shape:

762. Which craftsman always has a lot of **CLOBBER?**

763. What is the next number in this sequence: **17 19 23 29 . . .?**

764. Fill in the missing letters to find this stretch of water: **xHx ExGxIxH xHxNxEx**

765. Who can jump higher than a house?

766. Which of these is the odd one out: **box, tin, casket, tray, chest, trunk?**

767. Look at this magic square in which all the rows, columns and diagonals add up to the same number. Now fill in the missing numbers:

```
?  9  4
7  ?  3
6  ?  8
```

768. What do F and Paris have in common?

769. What is wrong with this statement: *The money you earn is called your celery?*

770. What do the following have in common: **sieve, funnel, colander?**

771. Use your tangram pieces to construct this pattern:

772. Which insect sits on a **THRONE**?

773. What is the next number in the sequence: **141 15 152 17 187**?

774. Which country in the far west of Europe begins and ends with the same letter?

775. What goes slower the further it goes?

776. Which of these is the odd one out: **bull, deer, unicorn, moose, skunk, goat, antelope**?

777. How can you use eight matches to prove that half of 12 is seven?

778. Why is K like the rump of a roast pig?

779. Can you correct this: *A young turkey is called a goblet*?

780. How can you lose weight in **CREDITED**?

781. Use your tangram pieces to construct this shape:

782. What becomes undone when it isn't **UNITED**?

783. What is the next number in this sequence: **123 987 . . .**?

784. Fill in the missing letters to find **TIBET**: xHx RxOx Ox TxE xOxLx

785. What turns everything else round without moving itself?

786. What is the odd one out in this sequence: **bud, bloom, leaf, stem, trunk, root**?

787. In which of these figures are X and Y further apart, (a) or (b)?

788. What vegetable does a donkey need to succeed in its exams?

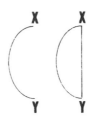

789. What is wrong with this sentence: *He's been in a dream during the last few daze?*

790. What do the following have in common: **Norman, Stuart, Tudor, Jacobean, Victorian?**

791. Use your tangram pieces to form this shape:

792. Who do you need to guide you through this dangerous **SECTOR?**

793. What is the next number in this sequence: **XXXVII XXXVIII XXXIX . . .?**

794. Which two consecutive letters in the alphabet must be added to frozen water to form two types of creature?

795. What is the longest word you can think of — one that gets bigger as you use it?

796. Which of these is the odd one out: **map, chart, plan, diagram, relief map?**

797. Look at this magic square in which all the rows, columns and diagonals add up to the same total and see if you can fill in the missing numbers:

45	32	31	?
34	?	40	37
38	?	36	41
?	44	43	30

798. How can you get on good terms with fiends by adding just one letter?

799. What is wrong with this sentence: *A hot rod is what you use to poke the fire?*

800. Which girl's name gives you a month in spring?

801. Use your tangram pieces to construct this pattern:

802. Who **RAGED** when his name was spelt wrongly?

803. Can you fill in this missing number:

2, 6, 20 . . .?, 63, 110

804. Fill in the missing letters to find this famous dining place: **xIxG xRxHxR'x RxUxD xAxLx**

805. What has four fingers and a thumb but is not a hand?

806. Which of these is the odd one out: **shirt, jacket, nappy, coat, trousers, sock, skirt, blouse?**

807. Study this pattern and fill in the missing numbers:

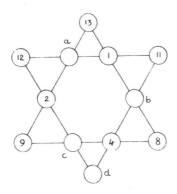

808. Why is U better company than any other letter?

809. What is wrong with this sentence: *When we went camping we slept in knapsacks?*

810. Use your tangram pieces to form this pattern:

811. What answer do you always find in **ULSTER**?

812. Who can judge when something is **IMPURE**?

813. What is the next number in this sequence:
0 15 30 . . .?

814. Fill in the missing letters to find this make of car: **xOxLx RxYxE xOxNxCxE**

815. What was the largest island in the world before Greenland was discovered?

816. Which of these is the odd one out: **red ensign, white ensign, Blue Peter, Union Jack, Black Peter, blue ensign**

817. Move three matches in this pattern to form four equal squares:

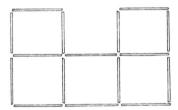

818. Why is your nose like the V in civil?

819. Which car is always found in **NEUTRAL**?

453

820. What is wrong with this sentence: *An octopus is a cat with eight legs?*

821. Use your tangram pieces to form this pattern:

822. Which political party dwells in **HISTORY**?

823. What is the next number in this sequence: **CLII CLIII . . .?**

824. Which sheep wanders in three letters on either side of O?

825. What causes baldness?

826. Which of these has nothing to do with riding: **saddle, bridal, stable, stirrup, spur?**

827. Which letter is it always time for in the afternoon?

828. Can you correct this: *Snooker is played with a queue?*

829. Which of these two horizontal lines is the longer the top one or the bottom one?

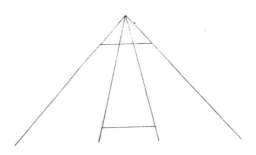

830. What do the following have in common: **London, Reading, Oxford, Windsor?**

831. Use your tangram pieces to form this pattern:

832. What did the king of **NIGER** do?

833. Which number between 1 and 10 gives you a tasty drink?

834. Fill in the missing letters to find this famous artist: **xExNxRxO xA xIxCx.**

835. How many sides does a box have?

836. Which of these is the odd one out: **Switzerland, Belgium, Denmark, UK, France, Italy**?

837. Look at this magic squares in which the rows, columns and diagonals add up to the same number and fill in the missing numbers:

2243	?	3142
3141	2242	1343
1342	3143	?

838. Which part of the world must you add to two bees to get public broadcasting?

839. Can you correct this: *The road was clear until we drove into amidst*?

840. Which piece of a golf-course can you find in **GREETS**?

841. Use your tangram pieces to construct this shape:

842. Why would the Romans have called Britain's first full-length motorway 1001?

843. Which letter of the alphabet must you pin either side of I before a baby can eat?

844. Why are horses never properly dressed?

845. What works of art are
there in **PIECRUST**?

846. Which of these is the odd one out: **Bristol,
London, Chester, Whipsnade, Liverpool?**

847. Move four matches from this pattern to leave
three squares:

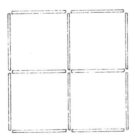

848. Which letter gives a northern river its name?

849. What is wrong with this sentence: *He went to hospital to have his ten disciples removed?*

850. What do the following have in common: **Audi, BMW, Volkswagen, Mercedes Benz, Porsche?**

851. Use your tangram pieces to construct this pattern:

852. What must you do after too many **SUPPERS?**

853. Which was the most recent year to read the same when it was turned upside down?

854. What is very bad but has to be added to a Roman 50 to make it legal?

855. What would happen to you if you swallowed your knife and fork?

856. Which of these is the odd one out: **swift, swallow, house martin, cuckoo, robin?**

857. What piece of an artist's equipment is this supposed to be: **EEEEEEEEEEEEEEEEEE EEEEEEEEEEEEEEEEEEEEEEEEEEEE EEEEEEEEEEL?**

858. Cut out four pieces shaped like the one below and then see if you can fit them together so that you form one piece the same shape but twice as large.

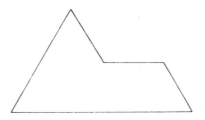

859. Can you correct this: An army dentist is called a drill serjeant?

860. What do the following have in common: **Curie, Einstein, Newton, Pascal, Archimedes?**

861. Use your tangram pieces to construct this pattern:

862. What do you hear when a **SHOTGUN** is fired?

863. What is the next number in this sequence: **11 21 41 81 . . .?**

864. How can you add a girl's name to the opposite of fat to use your mind?

865. What happens to tyres when they get old?

866. Which of these is the odd one out: **William the Conqueror, Richard the Lionheart, Charles II, King Arthur, King Alfred?**

867. Take away four matches from this pattern to leave four triangles:

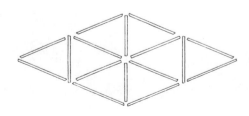

868. Why is X always well behaved?

869. What is wrong with this sentence: *Our visit to the zoo was grate fun?*

870. What do the following have in common: **enormous, huge, gigantic, large, colossal, vast?**

871. Use your tangram pieces to form this pattern:

872. What did one **SERPENT** give to the other **SERPENT?**

873. If daddy bull eats four bales of hay in a day and baby bull eats half as much in twice the time, how much hay does mummy bull eat?

874. Fill in the missing letters to find this American city: **xAx FxAxCxSxO.**

875. Why is a book like a king?

876. Which of these is the odd one out: **eau de cologne, scent, perfume, after-shave, tobacco**?

877. Look carefully at this diagram. Which line is longer **AC** or **BD**?

878. Which animal has four legs, rides in races and chases foxes but only has two letters in its name?

879. Can you correct this: *The supporters jeered their team when they won the game*?

880. What does a **LOBSTER** rest its head on when it goes to sleep?

881. What's this supposed to be:

D
L
O
H

Robbers sometimes organise them.

882. Which radio engineer liked the island of **MINORCA**?

883. What is the next number in this sequence: **2 6 12 20 30 42 ...?**

884. How can you ask yourself a question in **RENOWNED**?

885. Which years do kangaroos like best?

886. Which of these is the odd one out: **carriage, cart, wagon, truck, trailer, trolley**?

887. Move one match in this equation to make it read correctly:

888. What do these letters stand for **ICU**?

889. What is wrong with this statement: *Leg joints in young goats are called kidneys*?

890. Which British leader has the same name as a craftsman who often works on the roofs of old cottages?

891. Can you think of another word for **DESPOIL** hidden in the word?

892. Use your tangram pieces to form this pattern:

893. Which radio channel concentrates on playing serious music?

894. Fill in the missing letters to find this nursery rhyme figure: **xLx KxNx CxLx**

895. Why are false teeth like the stars?

896. Which of these has nothing to do with history: **museum, battle, future, royalty, church**?

897. Move one match in this pattern to correct the equation:

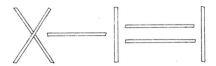

898. How can you make **VARNISH** disappear?

899. Can you correct this: *A long-winded person is one in good physical condition?*

900. What do the following have in common:
Turkey, Iran, Pakistan, Burma, Japan?

901. Use your tangram pieces
to construct this shape:

902. What would you find in
MANILA?

903. How can you make 5 by adding four to F and
E?

904. Fill in the missing letters to find this famous
London crossing point: xIxCxDxLxY xIxCxS

905. What is the difference between the North Pole
and the South Pole?

906. Which of these is the odd one out: **Times,
Telegraph, Mirror, Guardian, Mail, Sun, Star,
Express, Tribune?**

907. Look at this magic square in which the rows,
columns and diagonals add up to the same total
and fill in the missing numbers:

1	15	14	4
?	6	7	?
8	10	11	5
13	?	2	16

908. Which letter is the result of borrowing money?

909. Can you correct this: *Penpals are sheep that are fond of each other?*

910. What do the following have in common: **Connors, Borg, McEnroe, Smith?**

911. Use your tangram pieces to construct this pattern:

912. What is the next number in this sequence: **2 4 6 8 . . .?**

913. What do you buy cheap
SCENT for in America?

914. How can you put a kiss after three letters to make a practical joke?

915. What is black when it is clean and white when it is dirty?

916. Which of these is the odd one out: **New York, Chicago, Boston, New Orleans, Sydney, San Diego, Washington**?

917. Look at this magic square in which the rows, columns and diagonals add up to the same number then fill in the missing numbers:

$$
\begin{array}{ccc}
8 & 1 & ? \\
3 & 5 & ? \\
4 & 9 & ?
\end{array}
$$

918. How can you turn the **SAS** into a distress call by changing one letter?

919. What is wrong with this statement: *Every year I celebrate my birthday on 29 February with a big family party.*

920. What happens to the harvest after it has been **SORTED**?

921. Use your tangram pieces to construct this pattern.

922. What pudding will you find in **FLIRTED** if you look close enough?

923. What is this fraction as a whole number $\frac{100}{4}$?

924. Fill in the missing letters to find this popular film: xExUxN xF xHx JxDx

925. What kind of coach has no wheels?

926. Which of these has nothing to do with motor racing: **Grand Prix, Le Mans, Formula One, Suzuki, Ferrari, Silverstone**?

927. Take three matches from this pattern and move two others to form three squares:

928. Puzzle this out: **YRUSTUCK**?

929. What is wrong with this statement: *Thomas a Becket was a marter killed by four nights*?

930. What is the mechanic doing with the car until the **SETTING** is just right?

931. Use your tangram pieces to form this pattern:

932. How can you build something from part of a **REMARK**?

933. How can you add 6 and 50 in Roman numerals to one vowel to make something disgusting?

934. Fill in the missing letters to find this London station: **xHxRxNx CxOxS**

935. Can you correct this: *In the past soldiers used to fight in gherkins.*

936. Who always goes to bed with his shoes on?

937. Which is the odd one out: **scrambled, fried, roasted, poached, boiled?**

938. Which of these shapes is bigger?

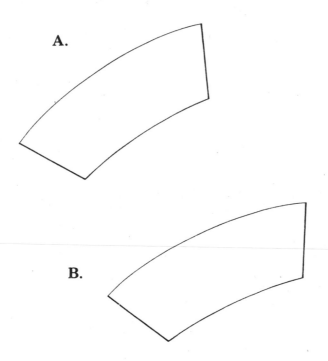

A.

B.

939. If this animal's name is CL, What does it feed on?

940. How can you find opposite of thin in **FEATHER?**

941. Use your tangram pieces to make this shape:

942. What did the robbers **STEAL** from the roof?

943. What is the next number in this sequence: 1 4 10 19 31 . . .?

944. Fill in the missing letters to find this famous queen: xAxY xUxEx Ox SxOxS

945. What is the difference between a pear and a pearl?

946. Take three matches from this pattern to leave three triangles:

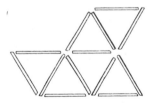

947. Which of these is the odd one out: **bath, shower, swimming-pool, car-wash?**

948. Y is Y like a greedy child?

949. What is wrong with this: *Cows chew their cub after they have fed?*

950. What music is there in **TAUNTED**?

951. Use your tangram pieces to construct this pattern:

952. Who teaches a school of **TROUT**?

953. What is the next number in this sequence: **7 15 31 55 111 . . .?**

954. How can you add the back of something to **ER** to form a six-letter way of getting in someone's way?

955. Why do postmen carry the mail?

956. Which of these is the odd one out: **lard, butter, cheese, milk, yogurt, cream**?

957. Look at this magic square in which the rows, columns and diagonals produce the same answer after you **add** two of the numbers in each and subtract the third. Can you fill in the missing numbers?

?	1	6
?	5	7
?	9	8

958. Why is L like a fairy with a bad leg?

959. Can you correct this: *I went to evening classes for the first time tonight to unroll*?

960. What do the following have in common: 1 2 3 4 5 6 7 8 9 10 11?

961. Use your tangram pieces to construct this pattern:

962. What happened to the boy when the girl **SMILED**?

963. What is the next number in this sequence: 6 39 78 95 82 4 . . .?

964. Fill in the missing letters to find this treasure: xHx BxIxIxH xRxWx JxWxLx

965. What is the difference between Sebastian Coe and an engine driver?

966. Which of these is the odd one out: **Swansea, Glasgow, Cardiff, Brecon, Fishguard**?

967. Can you think of a way of making six squares with nine matches?

968. What two letters race motorbikes round the Isle of Man?

969. Can you correct this: *The roman government was known as the cenotaph*?

970. What do the following have in common: **The Yorkshire Moors, Peak District, Exmoor, Dartmoor, Pennines**?

971. Use your tangram pieces to construct this pattern:

972. How many people row in an eight?

973. How can you add a three-letter vehicle to **MARRIAGE** without **MAR** to form another type of vehicle?

974. When did the mechanic fit the new **DYNAMO**?

975. What orchestral instruments would you find in your ears?

976. Which of these is the odd one out: **Southampton, Hull, Plymouth, Dover, Coventry, Liverpool, Falmouth?**

977. Which of these three straight lines is the longest?

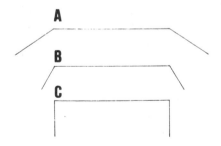

978. What are these: **CCCCCCC**?

979. Can you correct this: *Yesterday we went to see my father's nice who was very niece.*

980. What fruit is hidden in **MILLER**?

981. Use your tangram pieces to construct this pattern:

982. Which troops went to the **SEMINAR**?

983. What are six balls?

984. What two-letter word must you add to fill to produce a six-letter word with the same meaning?

985. What doesn't exist but still has a name?

986. Which of these is the odd one out: **doe, sow, mare, cow, bullock, hen, girl**?

987. Look at this magic square in which the rows, columns and diagonals add up to the same number and fill in the missing numbers:

23	10	9	20
12	17	18	?
?	?	?	19
11	22	21	8

988. What did the policeman say in two letters?

989. What is wrong with this sentence?

990. What board game is hidden in **TREADS**?

991. Use your tangram pieces to construct this pattern:

992. What is the **CLERIC** fond of drawing?

993. What is the Roman number for four when used on the faces of many clocks?

994. How can a woman and a creature of the sky come together to form an eight-letter insect?

995. How many months have 28 days?

996. Which of these is the odd one out: **Castle, keep, fortress, fort, defences, tower?**

997. Fill in the 8 squares below with eight consecutive digits (numbers from 1 to 8) so that no two consecutive digits are side by side horizontally, vertically or diagonally:

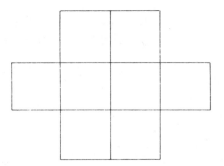

998. Which letter should you add to **CAR** to get very near a measurement of land?

999. What is wrong with this statement: *Puzles are eesy wen u no how they wurk?*

1000. For the final puzzle here is an old one that has foxed generations of puzzlers. See how you get on:

> *As I was going to St. Ives,*
> *I met a man with seven wives,*
> *Each wife had seven cats,*
> *Each cat had seven kits.*
> *How many were going to St. Ives?*

ANSWERS

1.

2. ASCOT

3. 10

4. WINNIE THE POOH

5. A ruler

6. 2 — one on each side

7. Only one hour — the alarm will ring at 10.00 p.m.

8. Five to one

9. 2

10. ||—|||=|

11.

12. ANDREW

13. 11 seconds

14. **Fur**long, furnace, furrow, furthest

15. Because the keys are on the inside

16. The letter E

17. Saturday also

18. 33

19. Arm, ram, mar

20.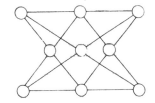

21.

22. PUPILS

23. Take seven apples from the bag and give them to seven of the children. Then give the bag containing the eighth apple to the eighth child.

24. Lewis Carroll

25. A bullseye

26. ANGLICAN

27. 3 socks

28. 729

29. Lord's Cricket Ground

30. TEN

31.

32. HORNED cattle

33. In the same place in which you jumped.

34. REDUCE, REDUNDANT, REDDEN, REDDISH

35. Because their hands are always in front of their faces.

36. West again

37. 1

38. Two hours

39. INSTANT COFFEE

40. The man in the portrait is his son

41.

42. The eighth

43. 101

44. SE — The letters are abbreviations for ten, twenty, thirty etc.

45. A pin.

46. Twice. Put three marbles on each side of the scales. If they balance the one left over is the light one. If they dip to one side, take the lighter set and place one marble on each side with the other in your hand. If the scales balance now you have the light one. If they dip you can tell which is the light one by the movement of the scales.

47. 38

48. Hannah

49. Neither — they both weigh one tonne!

50. 14 triangles

51.

52. Coolers

53. Ostrich — it's the only bird in the list that cannot fly

54. TOWER OF LONDON

55. Because it would be a foot

56. Make hay while the sun shines.

57.

58. $15 + 36 + 47 + 2 = 100$

59. THATCHER and ELIZABETH (the Queen)

60. TERN and TURN

61.

62. THICKSET

63. 95

64. Prince William

65. Hot, because you can catch cold

66. Denmark — it is the only one that isn't an island

67. NINE

68. 4 years ago

69. Julius Caesar

70. THE POST OFFICE TOWER

71.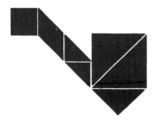

72. W — every other letter is missed out.

73. Tin — Nit (sounds like knit)

74. In the CELLAR

75. Because they spend most of their time in their beds

76. Ruler — all the others are connected with writing and printing

77.

78. 1 January 1901

79. 300 times

80. Ugly

81.

82. At the OUTSET

83. 157

84. Fair, fare

85. Shadow

86. Gibbon

87. They may look the same length but the horizontal line is longer

88. INCORRECTLY

89. 3 sheep

90. They were all American presidents

91.

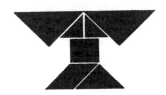

92. DRIEST

93. Mary

94. STRENGTHS

95. Growing older

96.

97. Toast — all the others have an animal name somewhere in the word.

98. Venezuela

99. 3

100. $\dfrac{22}{3}$

101.

102. On a SPOOL.

103. 15 17 19

104. Slow up and slow down mean the same

105. A porcupine

106. Date

107.

108. Alfie is the **taller** of the two brothers.

109. They are all hand tools.

110. F A J A O D — the letters stand for the 12 months.

111.

112. The EASTERN

113. (159) (258) (357)

114. The vicar read from a book of one of the prophets in the Old Testament.

115. By looking through windows.

116. Fighter

117. 35 squares

118. Between 27 and 28 hours. During the 28th hour he reaches the top and gets out without slipping back down again.

119. CARROT

120. They are all divisible by 6.

121.

122. PRINTERS

123. A

124. (1) Correct (2) The mistake in saying there are 2 mistakes!

125. It makes oil boil

126. Tyre and second

127. 47 triangles — at least!

128. 20 every time.

129. Eight divided by three will not go, but nine divided by three goes three times.

130. MENACE

131.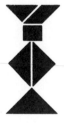

132. INGRID

133. 7

134. Million

135. Sixty

136. Maltese — all the others come from the Far East.

137. $||||+|| = \bigvee |$

138. Six dozen dozen = 864. A half dozen dozen
 = 72

139. PUPPET

140. They all begin ma . . .

141.

142. EATERS

143. By using Roman numerals: XIX take away I
 = XX = 20

144. NATION

145. C

146. Boeing

147.

148. Ten times

149. Unrefined oil is called crude oil

150. SAVE

151.

152. TONGA

153. 2520

154. OW — allow, owing

155. The cat

156. Marmalade — you don't spread the others

157.

158. 22 notes

159. 30 — the numbers represent days in the months starting from January with 31

160. Tablespoon

161.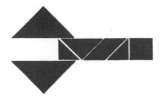

162. A day

163. 9 sheep and 18 turkeys

164. 10 rows

165. Tartan

166. On the deck

167. 30 — the others are multiples of 4

168. PAR

169. Queen Elizabeth the First was Queen of England

170. LIT

171.

172. SCARLET

173. 40

174. John Travolta

175. At the golf ball

176. Simon — the others are all names of English kings

177. The lines are exactly the same length

178. S + TONY = STONY

179. Danny's aunt and uncle live on a farm where they rear pigs and hens because the land is not fertile.

180. They are animals normally seen at night

181.

182. GATES

183. 20

184. LEGEND

185. A newspaper

186. Bamboo

187.

188. Champagne, turkey

189.

190. It should be 2 sentences — Charles I walked and talked. Half-an-hour after, his head was cut off.

191. COT + TON = COTTON

192. STRAIN

193. They all come from adding the previous number to the digit before it, ie: 9 comes from 5 + 4.

194. SNOW WHITE AND THE SEVEN DWARFS

195. Because they had to pack their trunks.

196. Platform and jetty

197.

198. His own.

199. 8

200. SAT + URN (sounds like EARN) — Saturn

201.

202. A duster

203. 18 eggs

204. EATING

205. They both grow down

206. Mediterranean

207. Form them into a triangle with equal sides and each side containing five dots.

208. There aren't any. How would Charles I have known for certain that there was going to be a Charles II. His coins would have been marked Charles.

209. 6

210. PAT + RIOT = Patriot

211.

212. NAMES

213. Four

214. Pass-

215. A funnel

216. ' + ' — all the others are punctuation marks

217.

218. Yes — December 31 and January 1 fall in the same year every year.

219. EVIL

220. The rain in Spain falls mainly on the plain.

221.

222. RESIGN

223. 3 cats as well

224. **The Empire Strikes Back**

225. On his head

226. Banana

227.

228. Horatio Nelson and the Duke of Wellington (Sir Arthur Wellesley)

229. Only once. After, you will be subtracting from a smaller number.

230. Ease — cease and please

231.

232. From hard-boiled eggs.

233. 7

234. LAD — BALLAD AND LADDER

235. The library. It has more storeys.

236. Clyde — the others are all English rivers.

237. 5 rows

238. The human crawls as a baby, then walks on two legs and in old age uses a stick.

239. BARGAIN

240. They all have to be cut after growing.

241.

242. Lager

243. When they make 11

244. Virginia Wade

245. Our footprints

246. Too wise you are, too wise you be, I see you are too wise for me.

247. Kayak — the others are propelled by wind. Balloon — because the others are propelled by hand.

248.

 four = square of 2!

249. The heart is an organ which pumps blood through the arteries.

250. ROW in BURROW and SORROW

251.

252. 48, 96

253. SECRET

254. TRAFALGAR SQUARE

255. Holes

256. Quartz

257. 35
258. 5 days

259. BRAN + DISH = Brandish

260. SLEEPLESSNESS

261.

262. Multipliers

263. You must bring her 2

264. Ant + Hem = Anthem, a musical number sung by a choir

265. Alone = ONE

266. Beech — it's a type of tree — not to be confused with beach

267. The lines are in fact the same length.

268. None. If it's a hole it's empty.

269. CAP + SIZE = capsize.

270. They are all words used to describe money.

271.

272. SELINA

273. 4368 or 2034

274. LET — VIOLET and LETTER

275. The sun

276. Pond. The others are areas of land.

277.

278. Better late than never

279. Queen Elizabeth the Queen Mother and the Princess of Wales.

280. GET

281.

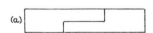

282. AMBLER

283. 38888

284. GOING

285. The date

286. They have all had something to do with music — even the vacuum-cleaner which was played in one very odd composition.

287.

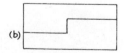

288. 'A'

289. Sewage should read Suez.

290. POST, STOP and SPOT

291.

292. FLARED

293. 5

294. TENT

295. A conversation

296. History — the others are sciences

297.

298. 11 — start counting T = 1, H = 2, E = 3 ...etc.

299. Shoals

300. New Zealand

301.

302. Tangerine

303. 100

304. Laurence Olivier

305. He picked up his tool-bag and saw

306. Windsurfer

307.

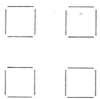

308. To get to the other side.

309. Own, now, won

310. They can all be made of leather

311.

312. SARDINIA

313. 8 and 32

314. ENGINE

315. Doughnut

316. Greek — the first group are all languages written with the Roman alphabet.

317.

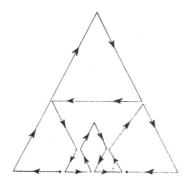

318. Wrongly

319. Executive should read Executioner

320. IDLE

321.

322. ERNEST

323. $1 \times 7 = 7$

324. Sherlock Holmes

325. When you are in it.

326. Curtain — the others go on the floor.

327.

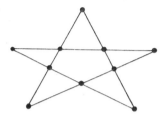

328. Your temper

329. Metaphor should read meteor

330. PRIMARY

331.

332. ANNIE

333. (249) (663)

334. WIT — NITWIT and WITHER

335. A horse and rider

336. Casualty — the words in the second group are to do with an hotel.

337.

338. Look before you leap

339. They are ranks in the Royal Navy.

340. SWEDEN

341.

342. STRONGARM

343. 4

344. SWISS

345. After it's been raining cats and dogs.

346. Raisins are dried grapes. The others are cereals

347.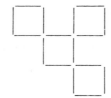

348. Christmas

349. Change vacuum to Vatican

350. Florence Nightingale

351.

352. BULGARIAN

353. $11 + \frac{11}{11} = 12$

354. MACARONI CHEESE

355. Water colour

356. The dodo is an extinct bird

357.

358. Stand and deliver

359. The car drove through the red light and did not stop.

360. Car-

361.

362. TUDOR

363. 127

364. Can Can

365. A bottle

366. Vinegar and honey, sweet and sour have been mixed here.

367. 6–10; 7–50

368. March

369. The mayor wore his chain of office.

370. China

371.

372. TURNIP

373. (834) (078) (555)

374. BOS + TON = Boston

375. A crack

376. Aluminium — the others all come from trees.

377. 243

378. July and August. (December and January are at either end of the year.)

379. The people who live in Paris are called Parisians.

380. Superman

381.

382. BENGALI

383. $1\frac{1}{5}$ or 1.20

384. Go to the dogs.

385. They become nags.

386. Blenheim

387.

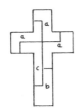

388. In the net

389. Base should read bass

390. EAR, ERA, ARE

391. Verily

392. 5 1

393.

394. Pea = P = Pop

395. Because they have no guts

396. Petrol — the others are solids

397. Sky high

398. He meant that they are opticians.

399. CANADA

400. 15 rows

401.

402. REDEAL

403. 4

404. FORD SIERRA

405. Your age.

406. Antarctica — the others are all mountain ranges

407.

408. The pilot

409. Alfred the Great, not Arthur, burnt the cakes.

410. All contain the letters a, e, r.

411.

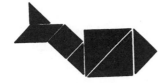

412. RECORK

413. (456) (654)

414. MARGIN and GINGER

415. On a watch face.

416. A warren is underground — the others are above ground.

417. The oblongs are exactly the same size.

418. With your nail.

419. Reefs should read wreaths.

420. DANES

421.

422. An accountant.

423. $99\frac{99}{99}$

424. MUTTON

425. The letter 'T'

426. Skin — the others are found inside the body.

427.

428. Robert Burns

429. Litters

430. NOISE

431.

432. SEALS

433. 13   6

434. Tea = T = Tablet

435. Noise

436. Leopard — the others are all types of bear.

437. (Fill in your own total)

438. Pneumonia

439. Both really. The fur comes from an ermin, but many ermin are vermin.

440. A SCREW

441.

442. THE STARLET

443. 15873 × 21 = 333333 and 15873 × 28 = 444444

444. PER — Kipper and Permit

445. Because he is lying.

446. Pebble — the others need to be mixed with water to turn hard.

447.

448. He was hit for six.

449. The masculine of vixen is fox.

450. The Polish

451.

452. Masons

453. 19

454. LEGAL

455. Because it is always dressing.

456. Even — the others are all 'placing' words called prepositions.

457.

17	24	1	8	15
23	5	7	14	16
4	6	13	20	22
10	12	19	21	3
11	18	25	2	9

458. NOD = DON

459. When we were top we were the best in the class.

460. DRAIN

461.

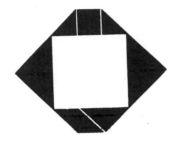

462. MARTIN

463. 49 64

464. Statue of Liberty

465. A tennis ball.

466. Telescope — the others are all used for carrying messages of some sort.

467.

468. A ring

469. The train was running fifteen minutes late.

470. BOBBED

471.

472. LADDERS

473. 4 7

474. CAT

475. A map

476. Sandal — the others are all hats.

477. They are the same height.

478. Charles Macintosh

479. A fjord is a type of Norwegian coastal inlet.

480. RUSSIA

481.

482. SEVERN

483. LIV = 54 in Roman numerals — **LIV**ING

484. FOOTBALL STADIUM

485. When their time is up

486. Tandem — the others are pushed, not pedalled.

487.

488. In Seine = Insane

489. Pemmican should read pelican

490. CAP + STAN = capstan

491.

492. The SHEIK

493. (168) (825)

494. CHARLES DICKENS

495. Your fingers

496. Marshal

497.
```
   215
 + 748
   963
```

498. SANDWICH

499. Conversation should read conservation

500. HEAL

501.

502. The INDIES

503. 55

504. ONION

505. 6

506. A novel tells a story. The others are all filled with facts.

507. Fold A to C to find the midpoint of the line. Draw a line from that point to B and it will halve the piece of paper.

508. Bell ringers

509. Sodium Sulphate is a chemical

510. They are all letters of the alphabet.

511.

512. REJAIL

513. 100

514. BUENOS AIRES

515. Because they have their own scales

516. Berkshire — the others are county towns.

517.

518. Wellington boot

519. Soviet should read serviette

520. INDIA

521.

522. REPOST it.

523.
$$
\begin{array}{r}
1 \\
1 \\
1 \\
+ 11 \\
\hline
14
\end{array}
$$

524. AREA

525. The letter F

526. Detergent. The others come from a chemist's shop.

527. Cup tie

528. The lines are the same length

529. Equestrians are people who ride horses.

530. PILING

531.

532. GRAHAM

533. 10

534. TOUR

535. The barber

536. The kangaroo is an animal known as a marsupial. The others are mammals.

537.

16	3	2	13
5	10	11	8
9	6	7	12
4	15	14	1

538. Because it comes in the middle of the day.

539. I like going on holiday but not when it rains.

540. All are breeds of dog.

541.

542. SLEET

543. 100

544. COPPER BEECH

545. When it is a greyhound

546. James — the others were the Christian names of the Beatles.

547.

548. S + CREAM

549. 60 ÷ 3 = 20 but 5 × 3 = 15

550. SEAL

551.

552. RACHET

553. (483) (294) (492)

554. BANANA

555. To run faster than anyone else

556. Oxford Circus is only an underground station. The others have main line stations as well.

557. Scotland Yard is the police headquarters in London.

558. All the horizontal lines are parallel

559. Samuel Morse

560. EAST GERMANY

561.

562. 64

563. ISABELLA

564. The Man in the moon

565. Parents

566. College — the rest are places of worship.

567.

2	9	4
7	5	3
6	1	8

568. Monsoon is a heavy rainstorm. Monsieur is French for Mr.

569. BIRO

570. PAKISTAN

571.

572. SINGING

573. 3 1

574. Tool, Took, Tooth

575. SA = essay

576. A stump is used in cricket, the others come from tennis.

577. The four are added to the five taken from the pile.

578. James Watt

579. Oxygen is a gas. An eight sided figure is an octagon.

580. NEAT

581.

582. The UNREAD

583. 767

584. TRAMP

585. Snow

586. Sahara. The others begin with G

587.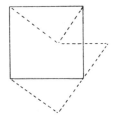

588. Bowler

589. A mummy is a dead Egyptian.

590. SUE + TEA (T) = SUET

591.

592. STEWED

593. 444444

594. RAT, TAR and ART

595. Because he wanted to rock and roll.

596. Trout. The others can all live in salt water.

597. $+ = |$

598. Nelson, who has one eye missing.

599. Lady Godiva rode naked through Coventry.

600. SAMPLE

601.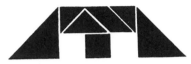

602. PLANES

603. 7 9

604. The Great Wall of China

605. By using condensed milk.

606. Reading

607.

6	7	2
1	5	9
8	3	4

608. Because it is the end of ski.

609. The Thames is the longest river in England but not in Europe.

610. REAL

611. REGGIE

612. $19\frac{1}{3}$

613.

614. CENTRAL AMERICA

615. A secret

616. Sun — the others are its planets

617. a = 1
b = 11
c = 12

618. They both come at the end of the alphabet.

619. The French national anthem is the Marseillaise.

620. They all flavour food.

621.

622. GUIANA

623. FIX – IX = 9

624. APE + PEA

625. Because she never marries the best man.

626. Boots — the others are banks.

627.

628. Faint heart never won fair lady.

629. Manual labour means work by hand

630. SWINE

631.

632. LANCASTER

633. 5 1

634. ENCIRCLE

635. Because he didn't want to get into hot water.

636. Cheese — the others contain flour.

637. It can be either depending on the direction from which you view it.

638. Because it makes an ear hear

639. Pheasants should read peasants.

640. MEXICO

641.

642. The slower

643. (483) (654)

644. Buckingham Palace

645. A coat of arms

646. Admiral — the rest are ranks in the army.

647.

1	14	15	4
8	11	10	5
12	7	6	9
13	2	3	16

648. Julius Caesar

649. The country is called Ecuador

650. CHIN

651.

652. CAMERON

653. 97

654. RUNNER

655. Safety

656. Minolta is a make of Japanese camera. The others are cars.

657. Turn the book upside down.

658. Wordsworth.

659. His name was Columbus.

660. KEATS

661.

662. Net

663. $(4 + 4)(4 + 4) = 64$

664. University of Paris

665. A crossword puzzle.

666. Jupiter

667. Try holding it in front of a mirror.

668. Face the facts.

669. Autobiography is a person's life story.

670. ZIMBABWE

671.

672. THREADS

673. (816) (825)

674. Horse chestnut

675. Bunny

676. Court — the others are places where you eat.

677.

678. Q = Queue

679. Cartridge should read partridge.

680. They are all young animals.

681.

682. OYSTER

683. 54

684. NAP — PAN

685. A dark horse

686. Paul — the others wrote gospels

687. They are the same size.

688. It comes at the end of Lent.

689. The earth revolves round the sun.

690. POST

691.

692.
```
  154
+ 782
  936
```

693. Because it reaps.

694. The Niagara Falls

695. A paratrooper

696. Lay-by

697.

698. J = jay

699. Hysterics should read Italics.

700. Elvis

701.

702. COLT

703. (816) (825)

704. ENTRANCE

705. Tomorrow

706. Juno — the others are signs of the zodiac.

707. 'e'

708.
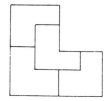

709. Hostages should read ostriches.

710. Abraham Lincoln

711.

712. Oriental

713. 11711

714. The White City

715. Your left elbow

716. Boot — the others are areas of a ship

717.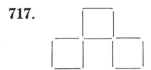

718. Y

719. I like to read magazines.

720. HEART

721.

722. GLOSSING

723. 15

724. Buffalo Bill

725. Spelling

726. Knife — the others are garden tools

727. They are the same size

728. Because it is always in order

729. Infernal should read internal.

730. They are all colours.

731.

732. GEORGINA

733. 1888 and 1118

734. LETHAL

735. The cannibal

736. Fridge — the others heat things

737. 17 squares

738. N and T because they form TNT

739. Water is made of hydrogen and oxygen

740. ROAD

741.

742. ONTARIO

743. $321 \times 9 - 1 = 2888$

744. HESITATE

745. An icicle

746. Rugby — in the other games the balls are all hit by something.

747.

748. Because 'we' can't be 'wed' without it.

749. A lightship is an anchored ship with a bright flashing light.

750. They all tell the time.

751.

752. CHARLES

753. 100

754. The Great Barrier Reef

755. Remove S

756. Motorway — you are allowed to walk down all the others.

757. E — because it comes at the end of life.

758. Retarded should be read retired.

759.

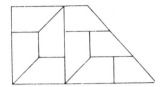

760. They are all types of meat.

761.

762. COBBLER

763. 31

764. The English Channel

765. Anyone. Houses can't jump!

766. Tray — the others all have lids.

767.

2	9	4
7	5	3
6	1	8

768. Both are the capitals of France.

769. Celery should read salary

770. None of them can hold water.

771.

772. HORNET

773. 25

774. EIRE

775. Money

776. Skunk — the others have horns or antlers.

777.

778. Because it comes at the end of pork.

779. A goblet is a drinking cup.

780. DIET

781.

782. UNTIED

783. 456

784. THE ROOF OF THE WORLD

785. A mirror

786. Root — all the others are above the ground

787. They are the same distance apart.

788. Pea (P) which makes an ass **pass!**

789. Daze should read days.

790. They all describe periods and styles in English history.

791.

792. ESCORT

793. XL

794. ICE + L = LICE + M = Mice

795. Rubber because it stretches.

796. Relief map — the others are flat but this has lumps in it.

797.
45	32	31	42
34	39	40	37
38	35	36	41
33	44	43	30

798. By adding R to make them Friends

799. Hot rod is a fast car.

800. May

801.

802. EDGAR

803. 42

804. King Arthur's Round Table.

805. A glove

806. Sock — it is only the article of clothing listed worn on the foot.

807. a = 3
b = 5
c = 6
d = 7

808. Because it is always the centre of fun.

809. Knapsacks should read sleeping bags.

810.

811. RESULT

812. The umpire

813. 40 scores in tennis

814. Rolls Royce Corniche

815. Greenland still

816. Black Peter — the others are flags.

817.

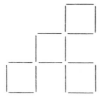

818. Because it comes between two I's (eyes)

819. RENAULT

820. An octopus is a type of fish with eight tentacles.

821.

822. Tory

823. CLIV

824. **ROAM**

825. Lack of hair

826. Bridal — the part of the horse's harness is spelt bridle

827. T — tea

828. Queue should be spelt as cue

829. Both are the same length.

830. They all stand on the banks of the Thames

831.

832. REIGN

833. 7-Up

834. Leonardo da Vinci

835. 2 inside and outside

836. Switzerland is not a member of the EEC, the other countries are.

837.
2243 1341 3142
3141 2242 1343
1342 3143 2241

838. A sea = C + BB = BBC

839. Amidst should read a mist

840. TEE

841.

842. Because MI is 1001 in Roman numerals

843. BIB

844. Because they wear shoes and no socks

845. Pictures

846. Liverpool — The others have zoos.

847.

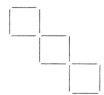

848. D = Dee

849. Ten disciples should read appendicitis

850. They are all German cars

851.

852. Press-up

853. 1961 — try it!

854. Lawful

855. You would have to eat with your hands

856. The robin is here all year round. The others are summer visitors.

857. E's L = Easel

858.

859. The drill serjeant is the man who gives marching orders on the parade ground.

860. They are all famous scientists

861.

862. GUNSHOT

863. 161

864. THIN + K (Kay) = THINK

865. They are retyred.

866. King Arthur — the others were all real English kings

867.

548

868. Because it is never in disgrace.

869. Grate should read great

870. They are all adjectives used to describe things of great size.

871.

872. PRESENT

873. None. There is no such thing as a mummy bull.

874. San Francisco

875. They both have pages.

876. Tobacco — You wear the others to smell nice.

877. Both lines are the same length.

878. GG

879. Jeered should read cheered.

880. BOLSTER

881. A HOLD-UP!

882. MARCONI

883. 56

884. WONDER

885. Leap years

886. A truck is self-propelled — the others are pushed or pulled.

887.

$$VI + IV = X$$

888. I see you

889. The kidney is an organ in the body not a joint.

890. Mrs. Thatcher

891. SPOILED

892.

893. Radio 3

894. Old King Cole

895. Because they come out at night.

896. Future — history deals with things in the past.

897.

898. Remove R

899. A long-winded person takes time to make a point.

900. They are all Asian countries

901.

902. ANIMAL

903. FIVE IV = 4

904. Piccadilly Circus

905. The whole world

906. Tribune is not a British national daily paper

907.
1	15	14	4
12	6	7	9
8	10	11	5
13	3	2	16

908. O = owe

909. Penpals are people who become friends by letter

910. They have all won the Wimbledon men's singles

911.

912. 10

913. CENTS

914. HOAX

915. A blackboard

916. Sydney is in Australia. The others are American cities.

917.
8	1	6
3	5	7
4	9	2

918. S/S — SOS

919. 29 February only occurs in leap years

920. It is STORED

921.

922. TRIFLE

923. 25

924. Return of the Jedi

925. A sports coach

926. Suzuki compete in motorcycle racing.

927.

928. Why are you stuck?

929. Marter should read martyr and nights should read knights

930. TESTING

931.

932. MAKE

933. VILE

934. CHARING CROSS

935. Gherkins should read jerkins

936. A horse

937. Roasted — the others are ways of preparing eggs.

938. They are both the same size.

939. Fish

940. FAT

941.

942. SLATE

943. 55

944. Mary Queen of Scots

945. The letter L

946. Car-wash is for cars, not people.

947.

948. Because it makes Pa pay.

949. Cows don't have cubs, they chew the cud

950. TUNE

951.

952. Their TUTOR.

953. 215

954. HINDER

955. Because it can't go anywhere by itself.

956. Lard. The others are produced from milk.

957.
2	1	6
3	5	7
4	9	8

958. Because it makes an imp limp

959. Unroll should read enroll

960. They are the numbers worn on the backs of players in a football team.

961.

962. He was misled.

963. Any number you like. It was chosen at random.

964. The British Crown Jewels

965. Coe is trained to run, the driver runs a train

966. Glasgow is in Scotland. The others are in Wales.

967.

968. TT

969. It was really called the senate.

970. They are all highland areas of England.

971.

972. 8

973. CAR + RIAGE = CARRIAGE

974. On Monday

975. DRUMS

976. Coventry. The rest are on the coast.

977. All 3 lines are the same length

978. The Seven Seas (C's) or the world's oceans

979. Nice and niece should be the other way round.

980. LIME

981.

982. Marines

983. An over in cricket

984. INFILL

985. Nothing.

986. Bullock is a male animal but all the others are female.

987. 23   10 9   20
      12   17 18   15
      16   13 14   19
      11   22 21   8

988. I I

989. Nothing

990. DARTS

991.

992. A circle

993. IIII instead of IV

994. LADYBIRD

995. All of them.

996. None — they all have something to do with fortifications.

997.

	3	5	
7	1	8	2
	4	6	

998. A car = Acre

999. Puzzles are easy when you know how they work

1000. Only 'I' was going, the others were coming!